Ketogenic Diet

An Ultimate Walkthrough
100 Fast, Healthy And Delicious Recipes

Contents

SECTION 1: FAT BOMBS

This section consists of balls, chicken skin crisps, rollups and baked avocadoes.

SECTION 2: BREAKFAST QUICKIES

SECTION 3: CHICKEN

SECTION 4: BEEF

SECTION 5: PORK

SECTION 6: FISH

SECTION 7: SALADS

SECTION 8: DESSERTS

SECTION 9: DRINKS AND SMOOTHIES

SECTION 10: DIPS AND DRESSINGS

SECTION 11: FROZEN TREATS

SECTION 12: MISCELLANEOUS

Introduction

I want to thank you and congratulate you for downloading this book.

This book will take you to the world of eating healthy and following a strict guideline with 100 delicious recipes of the Ketogenic Diet

The ketogenic diet is a high-fat, adequate-protein, low-carbohydrate diet that in medicine is used primarily to treat difficult-to-control (refractory) epilepsy in children. The diet forces the body to burn fats rather than carbohydrates. Normally, the carbohydrates contained in food are converted into glucose, which is then transported around the body and is particularly important in fueling brain-function.

This book contains a detailed overview on the Ketogenic Diet; The origins of Ketogenic Diet, Understanding Ketogenic Diet, A meal plan following the ketogenic diet, The top mistakes people make while going through the ketogenic diet and much more.

Thanks again for downloading this book. I hope you enjoy it!

- Chapter 1 -

What Is the Ketogenic Diet?

Is there a diet that allows you to lose weight while eating all the bacon you want? Is there a diet that keeps you trim and fit while letting you enjoy eggs, dairy, peanut butter, milkshake and other yummy favorites? Long-time dieters will probably answer No, because losing weight is often understood to mean depriving yourself of the kinds of food you love most. For too long, dieting has come to mean starving yourself.

Well, things have changed. There's good news for people who want to lose weight but don't want to give up "fatty" food. And this good news is the Ketogenic diet.

The "Keto" diet is not your run-of-the-mill diet program that prohibits the eating of all that's tasty and filling. On the contrary, it encourages that most of the food you eat should be rich in fats. This is revolutionary because for too long, people have been told to avoid fats because they make you unhealthy and, well, *fat*.

This belief has fueled the popularity of fat-free and low-fat food and diets. However, scientific studies have shown that low-fat eating isn't very effective for weight loss, and that it isn't really as healthy as we used to believe. The fact is that some fats are good for you, and some fats are necessary for good health. We won't be able to maintain good health if we don't eat enough of the fats that our body needs. Simply put, we can't do away with fats. It is a necessary nutrient.

In a nutshell, the Keto diet is one that recommends eating mostly fats, some protein, and very little carbs. To be more precise, the diet suggests that, ideally, what you should eat daily is 75% fats, 20% protein, and 5% carbs. (This ratio could vary, but it presents the general idea.) So, the Keto diet is a low-carb diet like the very popular Atkins and Paleo diets. But unlike other diets, the Keto diet places great emphasis on eating plenty of fats. This nutrient provides the energy the body needs in the Keto diet. Normally, a person's energy needs are supplied by carbohydrates (or sugars). Carbs when ingested are transformed into glucose, and this is what every cell in the body uses as fuel or energy. But since very little carbs are included in the Keto diet, fats serve as the main supplier of energy instead.

And here is where the term *Ketogenic* comes from. When the body doesn't have enough glucose from carbs to use as energy, a process called *ketosis* (or *ketogenesis*) kicks in, in which the liver produces molecules called *ketones* or *ketone bodies*. Generated from fats, these ketones supply the energy needs of the body. Moreover, they provide the energy needed direly by the brain. We know that if the brain doesn't get supplied with the energy it needs, we will die, very quickly and definitely. Additionally, the heart muscle also prefers ketones as energy source, and will use these over glucose from carbs if it could. So fats and ketones are very useful to the body.

Because fats are used up as energy in the Keto diet, they are not stored. Thus the person doesn't have unsightly flabs on the belly, upper arms, hips and other parts where fats tend to accumulate. This partly explains how the person loses weight when doing this diet. Of course, the process of losing weight is also enabled greatly by the elimination of carb-rich food in the diet. As mentioned, the Keto diet is both high-fat *and* low-carb. These two conditions are the essential characteristics of the diet that make it effective in maintaining good health and staying within one's ideal weight range.

- Chapter 2 -

Origins of the Ketogenic Diet

With the current popularity of the Ketogenic diet, especially among the young, trendy and health-conscious, it is easy to assume that the Keto diet must be a new fad. In reality, it came into being almost a century ago, and in a rather un-trendy setting, too. This happened in 1921, when a doctor introduced the diet to his peers as a therapeutic tool that could help cure seizures. The doctor was Dr. Henry Rawle Geyelin, an endocrinologist (one who specializes in endocrine glands and hormones) presenting then in the annual meeting of the American Medical Association (AMA).

Dr. Geyelin's thesis was that this diet he had developed could help treat or manage epileptic seizures. There was sound science to back up his claim. Historical evidence proves that food deprivation is an effective way to cure seizures. For example, the ancient Greeks had this practice of *starving* people, temporarily at least, as a way to get rid of their seizures and to help with other medical conditions. The Indians also knew that fasting or abstention from food and drinks was an effective way of treating certain diseases. With these as inspiration, Dr. Geyelin came up with a diet that induced low blood glucose levels (the effect of fasting) but didn't deprive the person of the energy that his body required. The solution he found was to provide an alternative energy source to glucose, and this was done by raising the body's ketone levels.

A few years later, in 1924, Dr. Russell Wilder of the Mayo Clinic came up with a similar diet that was also useful in treating seizures. He was the first person to actually use the term "ketogenic diet." This diet then became a popular therapy for epilepsy in the decade or two that followed its introduction. But not long afterwards, new medicines that could cure seizures more effectively were developed. They worked better than the diet, and were easier to administer, and so they became the preferred treatment method for epilepsy.

Many other developments before the 1920s or around that time also contributed to the evolution of the ketogenic diet. These include:

- Clinical trials in France in 1911 that studied the effectiveness of fasting and changing the diet to cure epilepsy. The final finding was that a low-calorie vegetarian diet combined with intermittent fasting was effective in helping improve the symptoms of epilepsy, and that this had fewer side effects than taking potassium bromide, the prevailing treatment used for epilepsy at that time.

- In the early 1900s, Bernarr MacFadden and Hugh Conklin studied fasting as a treatment method for epilepsy. A "water diet" proved helpful in many cases involving both adults and children with epilepsy. MacFadden and Conklin believed that epileptic seizures were caused by a certain toxin secreted in the intestine, and that long-term fasting dissipated this toxin. For a while, "fasting therapy" then became a common treatment method for epilepsy.

- In 1921, Rollin Woodyatt, also an endocrinologist, noted that the liver produced ketone bodies when a person fasted, or when he ate a diet low in carbohydrates and high in fats. The ketone bodies he observed were acetoacetate, acetone and β-hydroxybutyrate.

Decades later, in the 1960s, more advanced medical studies showed that the action of medium-chain triglycerides (or MCTs) could produce more ketone bodies in the liver. Following this discovery, Peter Huttenlocher came up with a revised ketogenic diet in 1971 that consisted of MCT oil plus more protein and carbs than were allowed in the original Keto diet. This new ketogenic diet was adopted in many hospitals as therapy for epilepsy.

It isn't exactly known how the medical therapy for epilepsy came to be used as a weight-loss diet for people who aren't epileptic or prone to seizures. Its low-carb feature, which is also characteristic of most weight-loss programs, is what probably lead health enthusiasts to experiment using it as a weight-loss tool. And when it was found to be effective, the Keto diet gradually became very popular among weight watchers.

- Chapter 3 -

Understanding Ketosis and How Our Body Uses Energy

Like any other living thing or complex machine, our body needs energy. It needs fuel to function. Likewise, every single cell in our body needs energy to stay alive and healthy, and to do its individual tasks. Without energy, our body's cells will starve and die, and our health will suffer as a result.

We get energy from the food we eat. There are three types of food that give energy: carbohydrates, protein and fats. Carbohydrates are the default or preferred source, because they provide a form of energy (glucose) that can immediately be put to use. When we eat carbs, such as starches and sugars, they form into glucose that is quickly absorbed into the bloodstream and, with the help of insulin, is transported into every cell in the body. As long as there is glucose in the blood, our body will use it for its energy requirements. Excess glucose (that's not immediately needed) is stored as fats.

Our blood glucose (or blood sugar level) can fluctuate, depending on what we eat, our activity level, and a few other factors. For instance, when we exercise, we obviously need more energy than when we're just sitting still. Our blood glucose during exercise can go down quite fast if we don't eat carbs to replenish the fuel we use up. When this happens, our body enters a state that's called hypoglycemia (low blood sugar).

Conversely, when we eat sugary food and don't burn up the glucose produced through exercise or activity, our blood sugar level can go up quite rapidly. We then experience what's called a "sugar rush" or a hyperglycemic state. We feel energized, alert and upbeat.

Fluctuating blood sugar levels isn't a good thing. It puts great strain on the glands that are responsible for regulating glucose. The pancreas, the adrenal glands, and the liver are all affected negatively. In turn, they produce adverse consequences that impact poorly on the whole body. Fluctuating blood sugar levels are associated with medical conditions such as diabetes, hypertension (high blood pressure), and heart disease.

What Is Ketosis?
After carbs, fats are the body's second preferred source of energy. When there aren't enough carbs or glucose available, the body will turn to fats for fuel. The liver breaks down fat molecules from food into

fatty acids. Some fatty acids are transformed into energy right away, while other fatty acids are transformed into energy-rich substances called ketones. The latter process is called ketosis or ketogenesis.

In other words, ketosis is the metabolic process in which fats are burned instead of carbohydrates for fuel. This is the goal of the Ketogenic diet: to use fats, not carbs or glucose, as fuel. And we want this to be the body's default metabolic state over the long term. Once the body becomes an efficient fat-burning machine, great health benefits can be realized.

As mentioned, the byproducts of ketosis are called ketones or ketone bodies. Think of them as the equivalent of glucose. As carbs metabolize into glucose, an energy source, so do fats metabolize into ketones, also an energy source. The great thing about ketones is that they, unlike fatty acids, can cross the blood-brain barrier. This means that the brain can utilize them as energy. Needless to say, the brain is an extremely important organ, and it has tremendous energy requirements. Although it is, physically speaking, just a tiny part of the body, the brain uses up about 60 to 70% of all the glucose that the body normally consumes.

Apart from making dietary changes, as we do in Ketogenic eating, there are other ways through which the process of ketosis can be induced. One is through starvation or prolonged fasting. The metabolism of people who are deprived of food naturally switches to the ketotic mode as a survival mechanism. Ketosis can also be induced when a person engages in prolonged exercise or endurance sports (for example, long-distance running that exceeds 24 hours) or any protracted and exhausting physical activity that depletes the body of its glucose stores. Pregnant people have also been observed to switch to ketotic metabolism naturally.

In a healthy person, there is nothing wrong with ketosis, even though it isn't our body's accustomed mode of metabolism. Ketones can provide adequate amounts of energy that the body needs, like carbs and glucose can. When switching to ketosis though, the person initially experiences a few side effects, but these vanish over time, and they aren't damaging to one's health.

However, there is a dangerous stage of ketosis that unhealthy people can find themselves in. It is called *ketoacidosis*, a condition in which there is an extremely high level of ketones in the body, enough to make the blood acidic. It is actually a life-threatening situation that often afflict people with type 1 diabetes, hence it is also called *diabetic ketoacidosis* (or DKA). For some diabetics, the lack of insulin in their body produces a hyperglycemic state (an abnormally high blood sugar level). Together, hyperglycemia and excessive ketosis make the blood very acidic and toxic. This is a life-threatening situation that necessitates immediate hospitalization. If the person having an episode of DKA doesn't get timely treatment, he could become comatose or even die.

The Three Energy Sources

Carbs are the energy source that our body prefers to use first, then come fats, and finally protein. Protein is the last macronutrient that our body will utilize for fuel, because it would rather use protein for other important functions. For example, protein is vital in maintaining and repairing tissues. It also provides structural support to every cell. It further supplies the vital enzymes that facilitate various chemical reactions in the body, and helps maintain acid-base balance. The amino acids in protein also work as antibodies that protect the body from diseases. Protein performs many other vital functions, and it is better used for these than as a source of energy.

However, when there isn't enough carbs and fats to supply the body's energy requirements, then the body is forced to use protein as fuel. This is dangerous because when protein in the muscles are broken down for energy, there is muscle wasting. Nutritional deficiencies are also likely to occur.

In the Ketogenic diet, it is thus very important that the person eats enough fats so that protein isn't used as fuel.

Of the three energy sources, fat is the densest and most concentrated. Carbohydrates, like protein, contain 4 calories per gram. Fat contains 9 calories per gram, more than twice the amount in carbs and protein.

Fat also stands out from the other two macronutrients in that virtually an unlimited amount of it can be stored in the body for future use. In comparison, only a limited amount of glucose can be stored. A healthy adult can store only about 2,000 calories (roughly 500 grams) of glucose from carbs. This stored glucose, called glycogen, is mostly found in the muscles, with some in the liver. After a while, the glycogen in the liver is converted into fatty deposits. Once fats have accumulated in the body, the only way to get rid of them naturally is to go on a low-carb diet, or to exhaust your glucose supplies through exercise, so that your body will have no choice but to use stored fat for fuel.

The Ketogenic diet is very effective low-carb diet that enables a person to get rid of excess weight *and* excess fat. It forces your body to burn triglycerides or existing fatty deposits, in addition to the fats you eat, as energy. When the body burns stored fats, the fat cells literally shrink in size, and this translates to visible weight loss and a leaner physique.

Ketosis At Work
When can one expect to see results after starting on a Ketogenic diet? The answer varies, but supposing you are healthy and not diabetic nor pregnant, your body's metabolism should switch to ketosis after three of four days of eating very little carbs. Roughly speaking, "very little carbs" means a maximum of 50 grams of carbs per day, which is equivalent to about two small bananas, one cup of low-fat yogurt, OR three slices of bread. If you don't eat any carbs at all—that is, if you fast—you can get into a ketosis state sooner than three days.

You'll know by observing some telltale signs that your body has switched into ketosis mode. These signs are important to know if you plan to adopt a ketogenic diet, as they will indicate that you are progressing toward your goals. Some of these signs may be uncomfortable or undesirable, but they won't last for long. They normally appear in the first few days or weeks of following a Ketogenic diet. For some people, they can manifest later, after two or three weeks of starting a Keto diet. Everyone is different, and every body reacts at a different pace to a new way of eating. What is certain is that after an adjustment period, your metabolic system will stabilize and these signs will eventually abate or be gone for good.

Signs That Your Body Is in Ketosis

Below are the common signs that indicate your body has started burning fats instead of carbs for fuel. You may experience a few of these, or all of them, simultaneously or at different times.

1. "Keto Flu"

Also called the "low-carb flu," this is a set of signs that mimic the symptoms of the common flu. The person experiences headaches, fatigue, nausea, sleepiness or lethargy, and lack of focus (or "brain fog"). Sometimes these are accompanied by digestive symptoms too, such as diarrhea, abdominal pain, or an upset stomach. All these can last for a few days, and are usually gone in two weeks maximum.

Doctors explain the "Keto flu" as the body's natural reaction to withdrawing from carbs. The drastic change in diet is bound to produce a reaction, and this is exactly what the keto flu is. When the body has adjusted to the change, the flu will be gone too.

These symptoms are also associated with dehydration and loss of electrolytes, which usually take place at the beginning of doing a Keto diet.

2. Decreased Appetite

Because they are eating fats and protein, which are very filling, people on a Keto diet tend to have a decreased appetite. The Keto flu (especially nausea) can also contribute to this reduction of appetite. Despite this, they should still strive to eat regularly, even if they don't feel hungry. It is very important to supply the body with all the nutrients and energy it needs at this time of transition.

3. Increased Energy

This is one of more positive side effects that a person can look forward to once his body has begun to adapt to the Keto diet. When the brain fog and the lethargy of the Keto flu are gone, the person naturally feels more energized and alert.

4. Bad Breath

This is an unfortunate but very common side effect of ketosis. The bad breath is caused by acetone, a byproduct of ketotic metabolism that is expelled as waste through the breath (and also through the urine). Acetone gives the breath a fruity or ammonia-like smell. An easy remedy for this problem is to chew on fresh mint leaves or sugar-free gum. It also helps to increase the amount of water you drink, because dehydration could also be a cause of bad breath.

5. Improved Focus and Mental Clarity

These are indications that the body has adapted to the new metabolic state, and is getting sufficient energy to fuel bodily processes. Ketones are an efficient fuel for the brain, hence cognitive functions may be enhanced.

6. Other Signs

These other signs are less common, but a person can experience them in the first few days or weeks of going on a Keto diet: a metallic taste in the mouth, dryness in the mouth, cold hands and feet, increased urination, increased thirst, and difficulty falling asleep.

- Chapter 4 -

How the Keto Diet Helps in Maintaining Fitness and Weight Loss

A cornerstone of the Ketogenic diet is fat metabolism, or the breakdown of fatty acids. This is the process that produces the all-important ketone bodies which supply energy to various cells in the body when there isn't enough glucose around to provide this energy requirement. But it turns out that ketones not only provide energy. They also fulfill a variety of unforeseen health benefits.

One of these benefits is the anti-convulsive ability of ketones. As we have already seen, doctors in the 1920s and 1930s knew that ketosis helps in the treatment of epilepsy, particularly in the management of seizures.

Ketones also help in the treatment of other medical conditions. As we shall discuss below, ketosis helps treat or manage type-2 diabetes, hyperlipidemia (high cholesterol), and various neurological and degenerative diseases. Of course, ketosis helps very effectively in weight loss, which makes the Keto diet very popular among weight watchers.

How the Ketogenic diet contributes to weight loss

The Keto diet promotes weight loss in three ways. First, the low-carb feature of the diet ensures that fewer calories are ingested, and therefore this prevents the person from gaining weight. Numerous studies comparing the Keto diet with other low-carb diets reveal that people lost more weight in the Keto diet.

Secondly, the Keto diet promotes weight loss by getting rid of excess fats in the body. Fat metabolism is significantly increased in the Keto diet, because fats and their byproducts, namely the ketone bodies, are needed to fulfill the energy gap caused by the lowered intake of carbs. As such, stored fats are utilized, including those in problem areas like the abdomen, upper arms and hips. The person also does not store any more fat because his body utilizes the fats that he ingests.

A third point that helps to explain why the Keto diet is so successful in weight loss has to do with how it manages hunger. This is a frequent problem with most low-carb and starvation diets. This is effectively avoided in the Keto diet with the inclusion of high-quality fatty foods in the diet. When a person eats fatty foods, he feels very sated, and stays that way for a longer period too. There are also scientific studies indicating that eating fatty foods helps to suppress hormones that are responsible for feeling hungry. Of course, the protein and fiber that are also recommended components of the Keto diet help further to eliminate hunger.

Additional Health Benefits of the Keto Diet

A good number of additional benefits of the Ketogenic diet have been documented in research findings and clinical studies. These include:

- The ability to fight cancer – Patients with gastric, colon and prostate cancers who followed a Ketogenic diet exhibited a slower progression of their disease compared to others who carried on with their usual diets. The same results involving animal subjects have also been observed. It appears that the diet helps to delay the progression of cancer. The definitive scientific explanation for this has yet to be discovered though. For now, doctors theorize that cancer cells, which require glucose fermentation to survive and thrive, are starved when the person takes on a Keto diet.

- Better management of blood sugar levels – Because high-sugar and high-carb foods are eliminated or severely reduced in the Keto diet, the glucose levels tend to be normal and steady all throughout the day. So-called sugar highs and lows, or dangerous fluctuations in the blood sugar levels, are effectively eliminated. Additionally, because the blood sugar level is stabilized, insulin sensitivity is also improved. This is of great benefit to people with diabetes, particularly type-2 diabetics, who long struggle with incidents of hypoglycemia, hyperglycemia and unhealthy insulin levels.

- A more efficiently functioning brain – We mentioned that ketones help along good neurological function, and can protect neurons from degenerating. They therefore help prevent diseases such as Alzheimer's and Parkinson's disease. Further studies indicate that a fat-fueled brain may be more efficient in many ways than a glucose-fueled one. Firstly, the former is healthier because it receives a better quality of fuel or energy from fats than that which glucose provides. Secondly, it also becomes less prone to so-called neuronal stress brought about by oxidation. Ketones have an antioxidant effect on nerve cells, hence helping these cells to remain healthy and functioning well even as the person ages.

- Chapter 5 -

Variants of the Ketogenic Diet

The Keto diet can be modified to suit a person's lifestyle and needs. As such, different versions of the diet exist, the most common of which are the following:

- Standard ketogenic diet (SKD) – This is the variant that most people use, and the only one that most people are aware of. It simply is a diet that consists mostly of fats (around 75%), some protein (typically 20%), and very little carbohydrates (5% or less).

- Cyclical ketogenic diet (CKD) – This departs from the standard keto diet in that it allows a break of one or two days during which the person can eat higher amounts of carbs than is typically allowed. Usually, a week consists of five days doing the standard keto diet, and two days of eating more carbs. Athletes and body-builders often use the CKD instead of the standard diet.

- Targeted ketogenic diet (TKD) – This diet permits the ingestion of more carbs when the person needs more energy, typically around exercise sessions or workouts, or during periods of unusual stress. This version is favored mostly by highly athletic persons.

- High-protein ketogenic diet – As the name suggests, this version of the keto diet includes more protein than is typical. The common ratio for this diet is 60% fat (instead of the standard 75%), 35% protein (instead of 20%), and 5% carbs.

- Chapter 6 -

How to Get Started in the Keto Diet and Some Tips to Help You Stick With It

If you're like most people, you'll agree that getting into a Ketogenic diet will be a major change, and not exactly easy. You're probably used to eating lots of carbohydrates for your caloric needs, and now you need to shift to a fat-based, low-carb diet. It will be challenging, especially in the beginning, but of course it can be done. Lots of people are now eating the Keto way, and there's no reason why you can't too. They're healthier, leaner and more energetic as a result of the dietary changes they made, and you can be too. Just be focused, and remember the reasons why you want to adopt a Keto diet, and you should do fine.

To get started, decide first if you want to dive straight into Keto eating, following all the rules, or ease a bit more slowly into it. If you choose the first option, you'll probably experience more of the negative side effects we talked about in Chapter 3, but you'll also likely see positive changes in your health (and weight!) sooner. If you choose the second option, which entails a more gradual shift in eating habits, it will be easier, but the physical changes you want will probably come a bit later.

Many people choose the slower, more gradual route because it is easier to follow and it prepares the body well for the severity of the full-blown Keto diet. If you want to do it this way, try cutting out one food group at a time. For instance, you could forego all sugary beverages (sodas, fruit juices, etc.) in Week 1, remove all sugary snacks and desserts in Week 2, and in Week 3 cut out all starchy carbs such as pizza, bread, pasta and potatoes. Then by Week 4, you should be ready to do the full Ketogenic diet. The general idea is to give yourself two to four weeks to slowly wean your body away from carbohydrates-rich foods, and then start a 100% Keto diet when you're ready.

Other people prefer to go cold turkey and dive right into the strict Ketogenic diet. If you feel you can last through the initial discomforts of withdrawing from carbs (which could last for days or weeks), and not give up the diet, then this could be the right choice for you.

Another decision that has to be made is if you want to count calories every time you eat, or if you just want to know the general rules and do away with the constant calculations. Some people feel more comfortable with a set target caloric intake for the day, and they want to plan their meals and snacks around the daily target. Others would just like know which foods are allowed and which aren't, eat what reasonably feels like a sufficient meal, and leave it at that. Either method is fine; just choose the one that better suits your personality, or that which you think will help you stick with your Keto diet.

What's important is that you do get a solid idea of the carb content of the food items you plan to eat. You should know which foods have high or medium carb content (stay away from those!) and which ones are low in carb (they're probably okay to eat in moderate amounts). It's recommended that you also know about the fat and protein contents of foods. This doesn't mean that you have to memorize any numbers. There are apps for mobile phones, and carbohydrate guides from books or online, that you can consult every time you want to check if a food item is Keto-compliant or not, that is, if it is high-fat and low-carb. The list in Chapter 7 of allowed and prohibited foods, and the recommended shopping list at the end of this current chapter, will also help you out. Feel free to refer to these guides or use any apps whenever you want to be certain of the nutritional content of any food.

Think over these things and decide how to proceed. Afterwards, the next steps that you need to do are to prepare your kitchen, and to get ready to shop for Keto-compliant food.

Preparing Your Kitchen

This means two things: getting rid of non-Keto-approved foods that you may have in your refrigerator or pantry, and restocking your kitchen with recommended foods. If you live alone, the first part will be easy; just throw away all the high- or medium-carb foods that you see. Remember to check the labels of beverages, sauces, oils and spices too. But if you share a kitchen with other people, such as family members who aren't going to do a Keto diet, then you probably cannot just throw out everything that's not Keto-approved. What you can do is to designate at least one cabinet in the kitchen as yours and yours alone to use. This is where you should put your grocery purchases (that are within the recommended Keto guidelines of course). This is also going to be the one and only place where you would get food to eat or to cook, and not anywhere else in the kitchen. It may be harder to divide the refrigerator into Keto and non-Keto spaces, but you should be able to work something out. The simplest thing is to just remember which food items in the fridge are okay for you to eat, and which aren't.

Here's a short list of common foods that you should throw away or donate (if you live alone), or that you should stay away from when in the kitchen (if you live with other people).

- Sodas, beer and fruit juices
- Candy, cookies, pies, cakes, pastries
- Ice cream

- Cereals and rice

- Pasta, bread, and bread products made from refined flour

- Potatoes, yams, carrots and all starchy or sweet vegetables

- Jam, jelly, honey, sugar

- Catsup and salad dressings

The general idea is to get rid of or stay away from carb-based foods, meaning ALL starchy or sweet foods. For a more comprehensive list of non-Keto-approved food items, refer to Chapter 7.

The second part of preparing your kitchen is all about stocking up on all the Keto-compliant essentials. This is necessary because you should never go hungry. You should always have food on hand that you can cook, eat or snack on. If you don't, you won't probably succeed in doing the Keto or any low-carb diet. One big mistake that you can't afford, and which a lot of dieters make, is to starve yourself to the point of being so hungry that you will eat anything. This will kill your diet, and it will be hard to get back on track.

With that in mind, take a look at this recommended shopping list and plan on getting these food items when you're ready to start on your Keto journey. You don't have to buy everything all at once; just choose the food items that you think you will want to use for the first week or so that you're on the Keto diet.

The Keto Dieter's Shopping List

- Fats and Oils – Use these generously in your cooking and meals as fats should make up most of what you eat.

- Avocado oil and avocadoes

- Butter, including coconut butter

- Coconut products: coconut butter, coconut oil, unsweetened coconut flakes, and full-fat coconut milk

- Olives and olive oil

- Dairy Products – Some creams and cheeses are allowed in the Keto diet, and these are:

  - Cheeses: Asiago, cheddar, cottage, cream, Mozzarella, Parmesan, Pepper jack and Ricotta

  - Creams: sour cream, heavy cream

- Fruits – Only a few fruits are permitted, namely:

  - Avocadoes

  - Blackberries, blueberries, strawberries, raspberries

  - Granny Smith apples

  - Lemons

  - Melons and cantaloupe

- Vegetables – Keep away from starchy vegetables, as they are high in carbs, but choose veggies that have high fiber. Fiber is technically carbs, but most of it isn't digested; it too is very useful in controlling blood sugar and lowering "bad" cholesterol in the body.

- Asparagus
- Baby kale
- Broccoli
- Brussels sprouts
- Cabbage
- Cauliflower
- Celery
- Cucumbers
- Eggplant
- Garlic, bell pepper, onions and shallots
- Iceberg lettuce, Romaine lettuce
- Mushrooms
- Scallions
- Spaghetti squash
- Spinach
- Tomatoes
- Zucchini

- Nuts, Nut Butters, and Seeds
  - Almonds and almond butter
  - Cashews and cashew butter

- Peanuts and peanut butter
- Nuts: Macadamia, pecans, pictachio, walnuts
- Seeds: chia, pumpkin and sunflower seeds

- Condiments
  - Vinegars: apple cider and white vinegar
  - Hot sauce
  - Mustard
  - Pickles

- Sweeteners and Extracts – Artificial sweeteners contain no calories, but they generally aren't good for your health. You can use them in lieu of real sugar, but it's better to limit their use.
  - Extracts: almond, orange, peppermint and vanilla extracts
  - Erythritol (either granulated or powdered)
  - Stevia (either liquid or granulated)

- Miscellaneous
  - Pork rinds
  - Unsweetened cocoa powder
  - Dark chocolate
  - Whey protein powder (sugar-free is best for the low-carb content)

Important Tips to Help You Stick to a Keto Diet

1. Drink plenty of water

Everyone needs to stay well hydrated, even if they aren't on a diet. The need for good hydration increases once a person starts any special diet, especially a low-carb one like the Keto diet. The person who starts doing Keto initially loses a lot of water weight, so he really needs to hydrate a lot to replenish the fluids lost. Proper hydration also helps to relieve some of the negative side effects that are experienced when just beginning the Keto diet.

How much water exactly should one drink? A rough estimate is your body weight in pounds divided by two, to arrive at the number of ounces of water you should drink at minimum. So, for example, if you weigh 150 pounds, you should drink *at least* 75 ounces of water daily.

2. Replenish lost electrolytes

As the person loses water weight, he also loses electrolytes that are dissolved in water. These electrolytes, or ions, are essential in maintaining many vital body functions. Salt (sodium) and potassium are the two most quickly depleted electrolytes in people on the Keto diet. To replenish these electrolytes, one should simply eat more salt by adding this to dishes or even to the water that he drinks. A pinch of salt added to a glass of water should be helpful. The person can also take electrolyte supplements, or drink homemade broths.

A simple home broth is made by adding soup bones (available from your local butcher or meat shop), salt, pepper and bay leaves to water, letting it boil, and allowing it to simmer for a few hours. Another broth may be made using a whole chicken and some herbs, allowing the mixture to simmer for at least 8 hours.

3. Plan meals

To achieve long-term success on a Keto diet, meal planning is essential. You could survive without this for a month or a bit longer, but if you want to go the long haul, do plan your meals. A weekly meal plan is a good idea, as is preparing (some) meals in advance and storing them in the ref. Schedule a time to sit down and plan the coming week's meals and list down the ingredients you'll need for them. Also schedule a shopping time to get these ingredients. Being organized will help ensure that you don't stray away from your diet.

4. Be prepared

Also have Keto-approved snacks available at all times so you'll have something to eat when you feel cravings or hunger. You could cook these in advance or choose low-carb saltine crackers, dark chocolate, pork rinds, nuts, avocadoes, celery sticks and the like. Many of the recipes in Chapter 11 provide great snack ideas that you can cook quickly and easily.

When travelling, it's important that you plan in advance what you'll eat. You may need to pack cooked meals, as it can be difficult to get Keto food in restaurants.

5. Keep it simple

Stick with meals that you can cook. You may want to eat something new and gourmet or elaborate every day, but maybe that's not very realistic. Consider your schedule, lifestyle and budget, and see what will work best for you, meals-wise. If you are too fussy or choosy, you could be setting yourself up for failure. Be open to the idea of eating the same breakfast maybe two or three times a week, and eating leftovers from yesterday for today's lunch or dinner. Also consider cooking things in bulk and then freezing the extra portions for other days.

Adopting to a new way of eating is already difficult in itself. Don't make it more difficult or complicated than it has to be, especially in the first few weeks. If something doesn't work, consider simplifying your meals or tweaking your plans to come up with a better system. Over time, you'll get the hang of things and the Ketogenic diet will be second nature to you.

- Chapter 7 -

Food to Eat and Food to Avoid in the Ketogenic Diet

We have learned in the previous sections that the recommended Keto diet consists mostly of fatty foods (about 75%), a moderate amount of protein (20%), and very little carbohydrates (only 5%). Based on this ratio, we will see in this chapter which foods are highly recommended or allowed in the diet, and which ones are to be avoided. Obviously, what we know from the get-go is that the permissible foods will be rich in (healthy) fats and protein, while the prohibited ones will be high in carbs and sugars.

Food to Avoid
Let's start with the food to eliminate from your diet, or to reduce drastically. These are the carbs that should make up no more than 5% of what you eat daily.

- All sugary food, including juices, soft drinks, (non-Keto) smoothies, chocolates, cakes, ice cream, candies, cookies, biscuits and sweet puddings

- Grains and starches, including all wheat-based products, breads, cereals, oats, corn, quinoa, pasta, spaghetti, pizza, rice

- All fruits, with the exception of avocadoes (which are rich in good fats), berries (like blueberries and strawberries), watermelon, oranges and cantaloupe

- Beans and legumes, such as lentils, peas, kidney beans, chickpeas and so on

- Tubers and root vegetables, such as potatoes (all types: sweet potatoes, white potatoes), carrots, parsnips

- Diet products that are advertised as "low-fat," "non-fat," "zero-carb" or "low-carb." These tend to be highly processed and contain artificial ingredients and gluten. Many low-fat products have a high-carb content. Obvious examples are diet sodas and drinks. Even chewing gums that fall in this category should be avoided.

- Alcoholic drinks, including beer and cocktails

- Sugar-free diet products, because these contain sugar alcohols

- Condiments and sauces that have high sugar content and unhealthy fats

- Processed food, including those that contain carrageenan (such as almond milk products), monosodium glutamate (MSG), sulphites (common in dried fruits and gelatin), and wheat gluten

- Artificial sweeteners, including Splenda and Equal,because they could cause sugar cravings and other issues

- High-fat food that have unhealthy fats, including mayonnaise, margarine, and processed or refined vegetable oils

- Milk, except for full-fat milk, but this should only be occasionally drunk. Most milk has high carb content.

The bottom line is to avoid high-carb or carb-based foods, including those that seem healthy such as tropical fruits and whole-grain foods.

Eliminating high-carb foods is probably the most challenging part of the Keto diet. It isn't easy to drastically change one's accustomed diet. In the beginning, the person would surely miss eating carbs, which are often our favorite treats or guilty pleasures. If taking them out of the diet proves too difficult, one could opt for a modified Keto diet. This could mean, for instance, a diet in which a bit more carbs are allowed in one or two days of the week, while a strict Keto diet is followed for the other five or six consecutive days.

It must be remembered that its low-carb feature is a cornerstone of the Keto diet. Its importance cannot be underemphasized. Even if the person ate a lot of healthy fats, but still ate too much carbs (more than the allowed 5% of the daily diet), his body won't get into a state of ketosis.

Food to Eat

Now for the good news. Below are the foods that are allowed or recommended in the Ketogenic diet. Many of these, when prepared right, can be quite tasty and sating, so they should make up for the deprivation from high-carb foods that one has to endure. You should base most of your meals around these food items.

- Meats of all kinds, including red meats, bacon, ham, steak, sausages, chicken and other poultry meat

- Fatty fish, such as tuna, salmon, trout and mackerel

- Eggs, preferably those from free-range chicken, pastured eggs, or whole eggs with high omega-3 content

- Nuts and seeds, examples of which are walnuts, flaxseeds, almonds, chia seeds and pumpkin seeds

- Butters and creams, preferably from grass-fed animal sources

- Cheeses, especially the unprocessed types such as goat, cheddar, cream, mozzarella, and blue

- Healthy oils, particularly avocado oil, coconut oil and extra virgin olive oil

- Avocadoes, which contain high amounts of healthy fats

- Low-carb or non-starchy vegetables, which include most green leafy vegetables (spinach, lettuce, broccoli), onions, peppers, green beans, mushrooms, asparagus, cucumbers and tomatoes

- Condiments such as salt, pepper, herbs and spices.

Apart from knowing what foods to eat and what to avoid, it also helps to bear in mind these general recommendations when doing the Keto diet:

- Eat *real* food versus processed ones. Examples of real food are meats, nuts, eggs, some vegetables, yogurt and a few fruits.

- Stay away from highly processed foods, as well as those with artificial ingredients, colorings, and preservations.

- Concerning what to drink, water should be on top of the list. Drink plenty of this. Coffee and tea are allowed, in moderation. Black and herbal teas are preferred, as are black coffee and coffee with coconut milk or cream. Wine, beer and alcoholic drinks are not recommended, though they can be enjoyed on occasion.

If you strictly follow the food recommendations above, it is often not necessarily to count calories or keep track of the serving sizes or weights of the foods you eat. Most people find that simply restricting the carbs they eat and eating more fatty foods (those with healthy fats, that is) is enough to bring about weight loss and a healthier, fitter physique.

Supplements for a Ketogenic Diet

No supplements are necessary, but some have proven useful especially for people who have just started to adopt the Keto diet. The following describes the most common supplements taken.

- Add salt to dishes, as this can relieve some water, mineral or electrolyte imbalances that may be experienced when shifting to the Ketogenic diet. An alternative is taking sodium supplements of about 3000 to 4000 mg a day.

- Additional mineral supplements can also help maintain normal electrolyte balance, especially potassium and magnesium. The recommended amounts are about 1000 mg and 300 mg of these minerals, respectively.

- MCT oil can be added to Keto beverages, yogurt or milkshakes. This gives additional energy and helps boost the ketone levels in the body.

- Coffee provides extra energy for people who feel weak at first from eating very few carbs. Black coffee is best, but cream may be added if desired. Skip the sugar, as this is a no-no in the Keto diet.

- If needed, exogenous ketone supplements may also be taken to increase the body's ketone level quantities.

- Athletes and very active people can benefit from taking creatine supplements and whey protein. These boost athletic performance, increase energy, and help in the repair and recovery of muscles and tissues.

- Chapter 8 -

A Seven-Day Easy-to-Follow Meal Plan with Breakfast, Lunch and Dinner Recommendations

To get you started on the Keto diet, here's a week-long diet plan that you can follow. Recipes for many of these dishes can be found in Chapter 11.

Day One

- Breakfast: Bacon, eggs and a whole avocado fruit

- Lunch: Chicken salad, made with olive oil and feta cheese.

- Dinner: Trout fish with asparagus cooked in butter.

Day Two

- Breakfast: Egg omelet with tomatoes, salsa, peppers and onions

- Lunch: Nuts and celery sticks with guacamole and salsa.

- Dinner: Pesto chicken with cream cheese, with a side of vegetables

Day Three

- Breakfast: Hard-boiled eggs, full-fat milk, tomatoes

- Lunch: Milkshake with almond milk, cocoa powder and peanut butter

- Dinner: Meatballs, cheddar cheese and vegetables

Day Four

- Breakfast: Strawberry keto milkshake

- Lunch: Shrimp salad with avocadoes and olive oil

- Dinner: Lamb chops with Parmesan cheese and broccoli

Day Five

- Breakfast: Fried eggs and bacon

- Lunch: Burger with salsa, guacamole and cheese

- Dinner: Steak and eggs with a side vegetable salad.

Day Six

- Breakfast: Ham-cheese-and-veggies omelet

- Lunch: Leftover slices of ham and cheese (from breakfast) and some nuts

- Dinner: Salmon with egg and spinach lightly fried in olive oil

Day Seven

- Breakfast: Low-carb yogurt with peanut butter and cocoa powder

- Lunch: Stir-fried beef, cooked in coconut oil and mixed with vegetables.

- Dinner: Burger with eggs, bacon and cheese, minus the buns.

This one-week meal plan can be modified by swapping the foods in one day for another day.

It is a good idea, generally speaking, to rotate the meats, vegetables and fruits that you eat over the long term. This adds variety to your diet, preventing boredom and monotony. Eating different kinds of meats and vegetables also provides different nutrients and benefits to your health.

Snacks

If you feel hungry between meals, don't hesitate to get some snacks. The following are some healthy snack ideas that go well with the Keto diet:

- Cheese (with olives if desired)

- Strawberries and cream

- Celery sticks with salsa and guacamole

- Any fatty fish or meat

- Hard-boiled eggs (one or two should suffice)

- Dark chocolate

- Full-fat yogurt or low-carb milkshake (preferably with cocoa powder and nut butter)
- Nuts

- Chapter 9 -

Frequently Asked Questions

Q: What are the side effects of the Keto diet?

A: In the first days or weeks, it is common to experience headaches, feel lightheaded and weak, be hungry and thirsty, be tired all the time, and even have sweating and chills. Sometimes these are also accompanied by confusion, irritability, anxiety, shakiness and heart palpitations. These are all classic symptoms of a low blood sugar level (hypoglycemia). This simply indicates that the body is feeling the effects of low blood glucose as a result of the low-carb diet.

Other common side effects are frequent urination, constipation, and mild acidosis or electrolyte imbalance. These are all temporary. As the person continues with the diet, his body will adapt to the new regimen and return to normal.

Q: Isn't ketosis dangerous?

A: Ketosis isn't dangerous at all, but ketoacidosis is. Ketosis is the state of the body when it doesn't have enough glucose to use as energy. To compensate, the liver produces ketones as an alternative source of energy. It is actually a helpful, compensatory process that helps the body to survive with very little glucose.

Meanwhile, ketoacidosis refers to a serious condition in which there is an excessive amount of ketones in the body *plus* a high blood sugar level. This makes the blood acidic and therefore toxic. Ketoacidosis is often a complication of diabetes, especially when the disease is managed poorly. It requires immediate medical attention.

Q: How long does it take for my body get into ketosis mode?

A: The usual period is 2 to 7 days. It depends on your body type, level of activity, and the food you eat. A tip to help you get into ketosis sooner is to exercise on an empty stomach. You could also restrict your carbs to 20g or fewer every day. Remember to drink plenty of water all the time.

Q: Is it possible to eat too much fat?

A: Yes, technically, but it's harder to eat too much fat than too much carbs. Our body tells us when we've eaten too much fats by making us feel sated and full. On the other hand, even if we eat too much carbs or sugar, we still could feel we want more food.

Q: Is alcohol allowed on a Keto diet?

A: Very little alcohol is allowed, occasionally. There are hidden carbs in alcohol, hence it should be avoided. But remember that liquor has fewer carbs than beer, wine and cocktails. So, if you must drink, go for clear liquor (not the flavored kinds).

Q: I lost some weight on the Keto diet, then I stopped losing weight. What should I do?

A: Weight-loss plateaus do happen every now and then, even when you are careful in sticking to the rules of any diet. Try out these tips to help you continue to lose more weight:

- Cut out dairy products completely
- Increase your fat intake
- Reduce further the carbs you eat
- Remove nuts, gluten, artificial sweeteners and processed food from your diet
- Check if you are unwittingly eating hidden carbs
- See if you could be losing inches, not pounds. You could still be getting trimmer, but you're just not seeing it on the scale.

Q: How long should I be on the Keto diet?

A: It is entirely up to you. Some people stop when they have lost the weight they wanted to lose. You can do this, and then do Keto again after a few months, for maybe a month or so, to maintain your ideal weight. Or you can adopt Keto for good if it works well for you.

Some doctors do advise that you shouldn't do the Keto diet for too long, like continuously for one year or longer. But there isn't any medical proof that doing Keto for life is harmful. While ketotic metabolism isn't the body's default mode, the body can adjust to it over time.

- Chapter 10 -

Top Mistakes and Solutions

Be wary of these common mistakes that people make while on the Keto diet. The solutions are provided in case you find you are committing some of these mistakes.

1 – Not eating enough fats.

Because of the widespread (but erroneous) belief that fats just aren't good for us, we may cringe at the very idea of eating lots of fats. We need healthy fats to survive, and all the more so when we are on the Keto diet because we are not eating carbs for energy. Watch what you eat and make sure that at least 65% of what you eat is fats. Some people even go up to 80%, and that is perfectly fine, as long as they make adjustments in their protein and carbs intake too.

You could also eat more of these excellent sources of fat to ensure you are getting enough of this macronutrient: avocadoes, avocado oil, coconut and its many byproducts (coconut oil, coconut milk, shredded coconut), MCT oil, fatty fishes, and fatty meats.

2 – Eating too much carbs

You could be eating much fewer carbs than before, but you still could be eating too much carbs. Remember that you should never exceed 100 grams of carbs daily, as ketosis won't take place when this happens. Most Keto dieters eat between 20 to 50 grams of carbs, and this should be your target range. If you feel you aren't losing weight after a few days or weeks, try eating fewer than 20 grams of carb. Don't worry about getting hungry, because eating fats and protein will take care of any hunger pangs or cravings.

3 – Eating too much protein

Generally speaking, protein is great for your health, and you shouldn't worry about overeating protein. More protein equals more health benefits, such as increased food satiety, better body composition, faster fat burning, and even faster weight loss. However, in the Keto diet, eating too much protein can inhibit ketosis. This happens when the amino acids in protein are converted into glucose, which then supplies your body with energy. This prevents full-blown ketosis to take place.

If you think this could be a problem for you, record your food intake carefully and ensure that you only eat between 1.5 to 2 grams of protein per kilogram of your body weight. This means that if you weigh 60 kilos, your daily protein intake should be between 90 to 120 grams, never more.

4 – Getting low on sodium and electrolytes

Some people are afraid of eating too much salt like they are afraid of eating too much fats. In the Keto diet, it's okay to eat more salt than you did before, assuming you don't have any medical condition prohibiting you from doing this. Put more salt on your food, or take salt and electrolyte supplements. This will help prevent dehydration and other unfavorable side effects of the Keto diet, especially for people new to the program.

5 – Giving up too soon

Any new diet takes time to produce the results you desire. This is especially true of the Keto diet. You may have to wait a while before ketosis kicks in and those extra pounds melt away. If you give up too soon, you won't see any weight loss. So be patient and stick with the diet for at least one full month. Don't give up just because you don't see any result right away.

- Chapter 11 -

100 Recipes

Here are 100 recipes that are 100% compliant to the Ketogenic diet. All these are high-fat and low-carb. They can make a complete meal or serve as yummy snacks to get you through your day with all the energy you need, or to satisfy cravings when they arise.

For ease, we divided the recipes into categories: Fat Bombs, Breakfast Quickies, Chicken, Beef, Pork, Fish, Salads, Desserts, Drinks and Smoothies, Dips and Dressings, Frozen Treats, and Miscellaneous. All these are self-explanatory, except maybe for the Fat Bombs. Fat Bombs are easy to prepare, bite-size food especially made for the Keto diet. They are high in fat and low in carbs. They are usually made of butter, oil, cream, seeds or nuts—all concentrated sources of healthy fat. The Fat Bombs recipes included here mostly consist of "balls," crispy chicken skins, rollups and baked avocadoes. You'll also find Fat Bombs elsewhere, as in the Drinks and Smoothies, Frozen Treats, and Desserts sections.

The recipes are numbered 1 through 100 to help you keep track of them.

FAT BOMBS

This section consists of balls, chicken skin crisps, rollups and baked avocadoes.

1

Curried Tuna Balls

Just a teeny bit spicy, these balls will tickle your palate and fill your tummy. Takes about 10 minutes to prepare, no cooking needed. Makes 6 balls/servings.

Ingredients:
- ◊ 3 ounces tuna in oil, drained
- ◊ 2 ounces cream cheese
- ◊ 1/4 teaspoon curry powder, divided
- ◊ 1 ounce crumbled macadamia nuts

Instructions:

Use a small food processor for about 30 seconds to process tuna, cream cheese and half the curry powder. This should form a smooth cream. Form this mixture into six balls. Put crumbled macadamia nuts and the remaining curry powder on a plate and roll individual balls through to coat evenly. Serve immediately or refrigerate up to 3 days.

Each ball contains:
- ⊕ *Calories: 93*
- ⊕ *Fat: 8g*
- ⊕ *Protein: 5g*
- ⊕ *Sodium: 80mg*
- ⊕ *Carbohydrates: 1g*
- ⊕ *Sugar: 1g*

2

Salted Caramel and Brie Balls

The tastiest dishes, thankfully, are the easiest and fastest to make, like this one. This takes only five minutes to prepare, and requires no cooking. Makes 6 delicious servings.

Ingredients:
- ◊ 4 ounces chopped Brie cheese, roughly chopped
- ◊ 2 ounces salted macadamia nuts
- ◊ 1/2 teaspoon caramel flavor

Instructions:

In a small food processor, pulse all ingredients until they form a coarse dough. That should take about 30 seconds. Mold mixture into six balls, using a spoon. Serve immediately and enjoy, or refrigerate up to three days.

Each serving contains:
- ⊕ Calories: 130
- ⊕ Fat: 12g
- ⊕ Protein: 5g
- ⊕ Sodium: 118mg
- ⊕ Fiber: 1g
- ⊕ Carbohydrates: 1g
- ⊕ Sugar: 1g

3

Carbonara Balls

A simple twist on an Italian favorite. Takes about 8 minutes to prepare, no cooking needed. Makes 6 fat bombs.

Ingredients:
- ◊ 3 ounces cooked bacon
- ◊ 3 ounces mascarpone
- ◊ 2 large hard-boiled egg yolks
- ◊ 1/4 teaspoon freshly ground black pepper

Instructions:
Chop bacon into small crumbs. In a small bowl, place egg yolks, mascarpone and pepper; mix well with a fork. Form mixture into 6 balls. Place bacon crumbles on a medium plate and roll individual balls through to coat evenly. Serve immediately, or refrigerate up to 3 days.

One serving contains:
- ⊕ Calories: 148
- ⊕ Fat: 12g
- ⊕ Protein: 8g
- ⊕ Sodium: 392mg
- ⊕ Carbohydrates: 1g
- ⊕ Sugar: 1g

4

Pizza Balls

A quirky take on everyone's favorite Italian snack. It's a great cravings killer, and 100% Keto-compliant too. Takes about 8 minutes to prepare, with zero cooking time. Makes 6 balls.

Ingredients:
- ◊ 2 ounces fresh mozzarella
- ◊ 2 ounces cream cheese
- ◊ 1 tablespoon olive oil
- ◊ 1 teaspoon tomato paste
- ◊ 12 fresh basil leaves
- ◊ 6 large kalamata olives, pitted

Instructions:
Process all ingredients except basil in a small food processor. It should take about 30 seconds for a smooth cream to form. Mold this into six balls using a spoon. Place one basil leaf on top and another on the bottom of each ball, then secure with a toothpick. Serve immediately, or refrigerate up to 3 days.

Each ball contains:
- ⊕ Calories: 82
- ⊕ Fat: 8g
- ⊕ Protein: 3g
- ⊕ Sodium: 96mg
- ⊕ Carbohydrates: 1g
- ⊕ Sugar: 1g

5

Hot Bacon and Avocado Balls

This recipe's hot, that is, spicy hot, when you leave the jalapeño seeds in. Take the seeds out for a milder taste. Tastes a bit like guacamole. Requires about 45 minutes of prep time, plus 8 minutes of cooking time. Makes 6 servings.

Ingredients:

- ◊ 4 slices bacon
- ◊ 1 medium avocado, pitted and peeled
- ◊ 1 tablespoon bacon fat
- ◊ 2 tablespoons coconut oil
- ◊ 1 tablespoon finely chopped green onions
- ◊ 2 tablespoons finely chopped cilantro
- ◊ 1 small jalapeño pepper, seeded and finely chopped
- ◊ 1/4 teaspoon sea salt

Instructions:

Place a nonstick skillet over medium heat, and cook bacon until golden (should take about 4 minutes on each side). Remove excess oil by drying bacon on a paper towel. Put aside bacon fat in a glass container. Let bacon cool, and then chop two slices into crumbles. For the remaining two slices, cut these into three pieces each; these will be the bases for your balls.

In a small bowl, mash avocado using a fork. Pour in coconut oil and cooled bacon fat. Add bacon crumbles, onion, jalapeño, cilantro and salt. Mix all ingredients well with a fork. Put inside the refrigerator for at least 30 minutes.

Take mixture out, and form into six balls using a spoon. Place remaining six bacon pieces on a plate, then top each with an avocado ball.

Serve immediately, or refrigerate up to three days.

Each ball/serving contains:
- ⊕ Calories: 181
- ⊕ Fat: 18g
- ⊕ Protein: 3g
- ⊕ Sodium: 258mg
- ⊕ Fiber: 2g
- ⊕ Carbohydrates: 3g

6

Sunbutter Balls

If you crave sugar, you will love these fat bombs. They only contain about a gram of sugar per ball, so it's a totally guilt-less snack. Takes about 20 minutes to prepare, no cooking needed. Makes 12 servings.

Ingredients:

◊ 6 tablespoons mascarpone (an Italian soft cheese)
◊ 3 tablespoons sunflower seed butter
◊ 6 tablespoons coconut oil, softened
◊ 3 tablespoons unsweetened shredded coconut flakes

Instructions:

Mix mascarpone, coconut oil and sunflower seed butter in a medium bowl until they form a smooth paste. Mold paste into small balls about the size of walnuts. (If mixture is too sticky, cool first in the refrigerator for about 15 minutes.) Spread coconut flakes on a plate or board and roll individual balls through to coat evenly.

Each serving/ball contains:

- ⊕ Calories: 124
- ⊕ Fat: 13g
- ⊕ Protein: 2g
- ⊕ Sodium: 43mg
- ⊕ Fiber: 1g
- ⊕ Carbohydrates: 2g
- ⊕ Sugar: 1g

7

Kalamata Olive and Feta Balls

A Greek-inspired recipe that brings to mind what it feels like to lounge on a warm sunny day by the Mediterranean Sea. Takes about 2 hours to prepare, no cooking needed. Makes 6 servings.

Ingredients:
◊ 2 ounces cream cheese
◊ 2 ounces feta
◊ 12 large kalamata olives, pitted
◊ 1/8 teaspoon finely chopped fresh thyme
◊ 1/8 teaspoon fresh lemon zest

Instructions:
In a small food processor, process all ingredients for about 30 seconds , or until they form a coarse dough. Scrape mixture and transfer to a small bowl, then refrigerate for about two hours. Form into six balls with the aid of a spoon. Serve immediately, or refrigerate up to 3 days.

One serving contains:
⊕ Calories: 61
⊕ Fat: 5g
⊕ Protein: 2g
⊕ Sodium: 135mg
⊕ Carbohydrates: 2g
⊕ Sugar: 1g

8

Egg Tapenade Balls

The French tapenade means an olive spread consisting of olives, capers and anchovies. This tapenade has chia seeds that give a crunchy, flavorful pop to the balls. This recipe takes about 40 minutes to prepare, no cooking needed. It makes 6 balls (servings).

Ingredients:
- ◊ 2 medium hard-boiled eggs, peeled
- ◊ 6 large kalamata olives, pitted
- ◊ 1 anchovy fillet (may be omitted if you don't like anchovies)
- ◊ 1 tablespoon coconut oil, melted
- ◊ 2 tablespoons chia seeds

Instructions:

Mix eggs, olives, anchovy fillet, and coconut oil in a food processor; pulse until mixed well; do not over-blend. Place food processor bowl in refrigerator until mixture solidifies (should take at least 30 minutes). Once mixture has become firm, remove from refrigerator and shape into six balls with the aid of a spoon. Place chia seeds on a medium plate and roll individual balls through to coat. Serve immediately or refrigerate in an airtight container up to 4 days.

Each ball contains:
- ⊕ Calories: 86
- ⊕ Fat: 6g
- ⊕ Protein: 5g
- ⊕ Sodium: 298mg
- ⊕ Fiber: 1g
- ⊕ Carbohydrates: 5g

9

Bacon Jalapeño Balls

A spicy Mexican treat. Takes about 10 minutes to prepare. No cooking necessary. Makes 6 servings.

Ingredients:
- ◊ 3 ounces cooked bacon, fat reserved
- ◊ 3 ounces cream cheese
- ◊ 2 tablespoons reserved bacon fat
- ◊ 1 teaspoon seeded and finely chopped jalapeño pepper
- ◊ 1 tablespoon finely chopped cilantro

Instructions:

On a cutting board, chop bacon into small bits. Then using a small bowl, combine together the following: cream cheese, jalapeño, bacon fat, and cilantro; mix well. Form mixture into 6 balls. Place bacon crumbles on a medium plate and roll individual balls through to coat evenly. Serve immediately or refrigerate up to 3 days.

One serving contains:
- ⊕ Calories: 135
- ⊕ Fat: 11g
- ⊕ Protein: 7g
- ⊕ Sodium: 408mg
- ⊕ Carbohydrates: 1g

10

Chicken Skin Crisps with Aioli Egg Salad

A dairy-free French-inspired treat that's rich and garlicky. Takes 5 minutes to prepare and 20 minutes to cook. Makes 6 servings.

Ingredients:
- ◊ Skin from 3 or 4 chicken thighs
- ◊ 1 large hard-boiled egg, peeled and chopped
- ◊ 1 large hard-boiled egg yolk, chopped
- ◊ 1 tablespoon mayonnaise
- ◊ 1 tablespoon fresh parsley, finely chopped
- ◊ 1/2 teaspoon sea salt
- ◊ 1/4 garlic clove, minced

Instructions:

Preheat oven to 350°F. On a cookie sheet, lay out skins as flat as possible.

Bake 12–15 minutes until skins turn light brown and crispy; do not burn.

Remove skins from cookie sheet and place on a paper towel to cool.

In a small bowl, add egg, egg yolk, garlic, mayonnaise, parsley and sea salt. Mix well.

Cut each crispy chicken skin in 2 pieces.

Place 1 tablespoon egg salad mix on each chicken crisp and serve immediately.

Each serving contains:
- ⊕ Calories: 79
- ⊕ Fat: 5g
- ⊕ Protein: 8g
- ⊕ Sodium: 252mg

11

Chicken Skin Crisps with Spicy Avocado Cream

Creamy, spicy, and downright filling. Takes about 5 minutes to prepare, and 20 minutes to cook. Makes 6 servings.

Ingredients:
- ◊ Skin from 3 chicken thighs
- ◊ 11/2 ounces (1/4 medium) avocado pulp
- ◊ 1/2 fresh jalapeño pepper, seeded and finely chopped
- ◊ 11/2 ounces sour cream
- ◊ 1/2 teaspoon sea salt

Instructions:

Preheat oven to 350°F. On a cookie sheet lay, out skins as flat as possible.

Bake 12–15 minutes until skins turn light brown and crispy; do not burn the skins.

Remove skins from cookie sheet and place on a paper towel to cool.

In a small bowl, combine avocado pulp, sour cream, jalapeño, and sea salt. Mix until well blended.

Cut each crispy chicken skin in 2 pieces.

Place 1 tablespoon avocado mix on each chicken crisp and serve immediately.

Each serving contains:
- ⊕ Calories: 66
- ⊕ Fat: 4g
- ⊕ Protein: 7g
- ⊕ Sodium: 232mg
- ⊕ Fiber: 1g
- ⊕ Carbohydrates: 1g

12

Chicken Skin Crisps Satay

A Thai-inspired delight. Takes about 5 minutes to prepare, plus 20 minutes cooking time. Makes 6 servings.

Ingredients:
- ◊ Skin from 3-4 chicken thighs
- ◊ 2 tablespoons chunky peanut butter
- ◊ 1 teaspoon coconut oil
- ◊ 1 tablespoon coconut cream
- ◊ 1 teaspoon fresh jalapeño pepper, seeded and minced
- ◊ 1/4 garlic clove, minced
- ◊ 1 teaspoon coconut aminos

Instructions:

Preheat oven to 350°F. On a cookie sheet, lay out skins as flat as possible. Bake 12–15 minutes or until skins turn light brown and crispy. Be careful not to burn the skins. Remove skins from cookie sheet and place on a paper towel to cool.

In a small food processor, add peanut butter, coconut oil, jalapeños, coconut cream, garlic and coconut aminos.

Mix about 30 seconds until well blended.

Cut each crispy chicken skin in 2 pieces.

Place 1 tablespoon peanut sauce on each chicken crisp and serve immediately. If sauce is too runny, refrigerate 2 hours before using.

Each serving contains:
- ⊕ Calories: 91
- ⊕ Fat: 5g
- ⊕ Protein: 8g
- ⊕ Sodium: 105mg
- ⊕ Carbohydrates: 3g
- ⊕ Sugar: 2g

13

Chicken Skin Crisps Alfredo

A tasty snack with the well-loved Alfredo sauce, minus the carbs. Takes 5 minutes prep time and 20 minutes cooking time. Makes 6 servings.

Ingredients:
- ◊ Skin from 3-4 chicken thighs
- ◊ 2 tablespoons ricotta
- ◊ 2 tablespoons cream cheese
- ◊ 1 tablespoon Parmesan, grated
- ◊ 1/4 teaspoon ground white pepper
- ◊ 1/4 garlic clove, minced

Instructions:

Preheat oven to 350°F. On a cookie sheet, lay out skins as flat as possible.

Bake 12–15 minutes until skins turn light brown and crispy; do not burn the skins.

Remove skins from cookie sheet and place on a paper towel to cool.

In a small bowl, add cheeses, pepper and garlic. Mix until well blended.

Cut each crispy chicken skin in 2 pieces.

Place 1 tablespoon Alfredo cheese mix on each chicken crisp and serve immediately.

One serving contains:

- ⊕ Calories: 71
- ⊕ Fat: 4g
- ⊕ Protein: 8g
- ⊕ Sodium: 65mg
- ⊕ Carbohydrates: 1g

14

Simplest Salami Roll-Ups

Ingredients:
- ◊ 5 large slices hard salami
- ◊ 1 tablespoon cream cheese
- ◊ 2 celery stalks

Instructions:

Soften cream cheese in microwave.

Spread cream cheese on each salami slice, and roll them up.

Serve with celery on the side.

One serving contais:
- ⊕ Total net carbs: 5.9 g

15

Salami and Olive Rollups

A tasty Keto-compliant twist on an Italian favorite. Takes 5 minutes to prepare, no cooking required. Makes 3 servings.

Ingredients:
- ◊   12 large kalamata olives, pitted
- ◊   3 ounces cream cheese
- ◊   3 (1-ounce) slices Italian salami

Instructions:

In a small food processor, for about 10 seconds, mix olives and cream cheese to form a coarse dough.

Form cheese mixture into 3 balls using a spoon.

Place each ball on a slice of salami, then roll salami around it and secure with a toothpick.

Serve immediately or refrigerate up to 3 days.

Each serving contains:
- ⊕   Calories: 233
- ⊕   Fat: 20g
- ⊕   Protein: 8g
- ⊕   Sodium: 621mg
- ⊕   Fiber: 0g
- ⊕   Carbohydrates: 6g
- ⊕   Sugar: 1g

16

Mediterranean Rollups

A dairy-free, Greek-inspired treat. Takes 7 minutes to prepare and 3 minutes to cook. Makes 2 servings.

Ingredients:
◊   1 large egg
◊   6 large kalamata olives, pitted
◊   1 tablespoon extra-virgin olive oil
◊   1 ounce sun-dried tomatoes in oil
◊   1/8 teaspoon red chili flakes
◊   1/8 teaspoon parsley flakes
◊   1/8 teaspoon sea salt

Instructions:

In a small bowl, combine egg, olive oil, and salt. Whisk until foamy.

Get a small nonstick pan and heat over high heat. Pour in egg mixture, spreading evenly to form a thin, even layer.

Cook first side for about 1 minute, then flip frittata. Cook second side until golden on bottom, for about 2 more minutes.

Remove and transfer frittata to a plate.

In a small food processor, mix olives, chili flakes, tomatoes and parsley until well chopped and blended. This should take about 30 seconds.

Spread olive paste on top of frittata in an even layer.

Roll frittata into a tight roll, cut into 2 pieces, and serve immediately.

Each serving contains:
   ⊕ Calories: 153
   ⊕ Fat: 10g
   ⊕ Protein: 5g
   ⊕ Sodium: 478mg
   ⊕ Fiber: 2g
   ⊕ Carbohydrates: 14g
   ⊕ Sugar: 5g

17

Smoked Salmon and Crème Fraîche Rollups

A great substitute for bagel and lox for breakfast or brunch. Takes only 5 minutes to prepare, no cooking needed. Makes 3 servings.

Ingredients:

◊ 3 ounces crème fraîche (French sour cream)
◊ 1/8 teaspoon fresh lemon zest
◊ 3 slices smoked salmon (lox), about 1 ounce each

Instructions:

In a small bowl, mix crème fraîche and lemon zest.

Spread 1/3 mixture on top of each salmon slice.

Roll slices into individual rolls and secure with a toothpick.

Serve immediately.

Each serving contains:

⊕ Calories: 87
⊕ Fat: 7g
⊕ Protein: 6g
⊕ Sodium: 245mg
⊕ Carbohydrates: 8g
⊕ Sugar: 1g

18

Basic Baked Egg Avocado

Another simple and easy recipe for a quick but satisfying breakfast or snack. Takes 10 minutes to prepare, plus 20 minutes to cook. Makes 2 servings.

Ingredients:
- ◊ 1 medium avocado, halved and pitted (keep skin on)
- ◊ 2 large egg yolks
- ◊ 2 teaspoons mayonnaise
- ◊ 1/4 teaspoon freshly ground black pepper

Instructions:

Preheat oven to 350°F.

Put avocado halves hole-side up in a shallow ovenproof dish.

Place 1 egg yolk into each avocado cavity.

Mix mayonnaise and black pepper in a small bowl, and then place mixture on the two avocado halves, gently on top of each egg yolk, taking care not to break the yolk.

Bake for 20 minutes. Serve hot.

An alternative is to swirl together the mayonnaise and egg yolk inside the avocado hole.

Each serving contains:

- ⊕ Calories: 248
- ⊕ Fat: 23g
- ⊕ Protein: 5g
- ⊕ Sodium: 41mg
- ⊕ Fiber: 7g
- ⊕ Carbohydrates: 9g
- ⊕ Sugar: 8g

19

Baked Avocado with Blue Cheese

A super easy recipe that yields a most flavorful snack. Takes about 10 minutes to prepare, plus 20 minutes to cook. Makes 2 servings.

Ingredients:
◊ 1 medium avocado, halved and pitted, skin on
◊ 2 ounces crumbled blue cheese
◊ 1 tablespoon butter, softened

Instructions:
Preheat oven to 350°F.

Put avocado halves hole-side up in a shallow baking dish.

In a small bowl, mix butter and blue cheese.

Place 1/2 mixture into each avocado cavity.

Bake for about 20 minutes. Serve hot.

Each serving contains:
⊕ Calories: 310
⊕ Fat: 28g
⊕ Protein: 8g
⊕ Sodium: 398mg
⊕ Fiber: 7g
⊕ Carbohydrates: 9g
⊕ Sugar: 1g

20

Savory-Sweet Baked Avocado with Pecans and Coconut

Savory, sweet yet sugar-free. Takes about 10 minutes to prepare, plus 20 minutes to cook. Makes 2 servings.

Ingredients:
- ◊ 1 medium avocado, halved and pitted, skin on
- ◊ 2 tablespoons grated unsweetened coconut
- ◊ 2 tablespoons coconut oil
- ◊ 6 pecan halves

Instructions:

Preheat oven to 350°F.

Put avocado halves hole-side up in a small, shallow baking dish.

In a small bowl, mix grated coconut with coconut oil. Scoop mixture into each avocado cavity.

Carefully place 3 pecans on top of each avocado half.

Bake for 20 minutes. Serve immediately, or refrigerate first if a cold dish is preferred.

Each serving contains:

- ⊕ Calories: 328
- ⊕ Fat: 33g
- ⊕ Protein: 3g
- ⊕ Sodium: 8mg
- ⊕ Fiber: 8g
- ⊕ Carbohydrates: 10g
- ⊕ Sugar: 1g

21

Crab Dynamite Baked Avocado

A dairy-free, Japanese-inspired concoction to tickle the palate and relieve any cravings. Takes 10 minutes to prepare, plus 20 minutes to cook. Makes 2 servings.

Ingredients

◊ 1 medium avocado, halved and pitted (leave the skin on)
◊ 11/2 ounces real crabmeat, drained (no juices)
◊ 2 teaspoons mayonnaise
◊ 1 teaspoon coconut aminos, soy sauce, or tamari
◊ 1/4 teaspoon freshly ground black pepper

Instructions:

Preheat oven to 350°F.

Place avocado halves hole-side up in a shallow baking dish.

In a small bowl, combine crabmeat, coconut aminos, mayonnaise, and pepper, then divide and scoop into each avocado cavity.

Bake for 20 minutes. Serve hot.

Each serving contains:

- ⊕ Calories: 217
- ⊕ Fat: 19g
- ⊕ Protein: 7g
- ⊕ Sodium: 253mg
- ⊕ Fiber: 7g
- ⊕ Carbohydrates: 9g
- ⊕ Sugar: 1g

- SECTION 2 -

BREAKFAST QUICKIES

22

Sausage, Egg and Cheese

(Makes 1 serving)

Ingredients:
- ◇ 3 oz. breakfast sausage
- ◇ 1 large egg
- ◇ 1 tablespoon olive oil
- ◇ 1 slice Cheddar cheese
- ◇ Green onion or chives as garnishing

Instructions:

Grease pan with olive oil, and cook the breakfast sausage and egg (over easy).

Add a slice of cheddar, and layer or arrange the ingredients as you please.

Drizzle with some hot sauce if desired.

Top with chives or green onion.

A serving contains:
- ⊕ Calories: 574
- ⊕ Fat: 49g
- ⊕ Protein: 27g
- ⊕ Carbs: 1g

23

Fried Eggs with Red Wine Vinegar

(Makes 2 servings)

Ingredients:
- ◊ 4 eggs
- ◊ 1 tablespoon butter
- ◊ 2 teaspoons red wine vinegar
- ◊ ¼ teaspoon salt
- ◊ 1/8 teaspoon pepper
- ◊ 1/8 teaspoon marjoram
- ◊ ¼ teaspoon parsley

Instructions:

Melt ½ tablespoon butter on skillet, and break eggs in.

Add spices and cook until egg whites set. Place eggs on a serving plate.

Melt remaining butter on same skillet and heat for two minutes. Stir in red wine vinegar, and let mixture cook for another minute. Pour this over eggs. Garnish with parsley.

One serving contains:
- ⊕ Total net carbs: 1 gram

24

Pepperoni Pizza Omelette

(Makes 1 serving)

Ingredients:

- ◊ 3 large eggs
- ◊ ½ oz. pepperoni slices
- ◊ 2 strips of bacon
- ◊ 1 tablespoon heavy cream
- ◊ ½ cup shredded mozzarella cheese
- ◊ Salt and pepper
- ◊ Basil
- ◊ Oil to grease pan

Instructions:

Fry the bacon strips in a pan (or bake them if desired).

Place oil in another pan and heat on medium flame.

Beat eggs, add heavy cream, mix, and pour into the hot pan. Let all cook until almost done.

Add on one side some pepperoni slices.

Over the pepperoni, sprinkle cheese, then salt, pepper and basil. Fold the omelet over.

Let cook for one more minute. Serve omelette with the bacon on the side.

One serving contains:

- ⊕ Calories: 600
- ⊕ Fat: 53g
- ⊕ Protein: 32g
- ⊕ Carbs: 5g

25

Classic Creamy Scrambled Eggs

(Makes 2 servings)

Ingredients:
- ◊ 6 large eggs
- ◊ 6 strips bacon
- ◊ 2 tablespoon butter
- ◊ 2 tablespoon sour cream
- ◊ 1/3 teaspoon salt
- ◊ ½ teaspoon black pepper
- ◊ 2 stalks green onion, chopped

Instructions:

Melt butter on a pan over medium-high heat.

Crack eggs on pan. Stir continuously. Alternate doing this on the heat and off, in 30 second intervals. Turn heat off when eggs are almost done, and leave eggs on pan to continue cooking with the residual heat. Add sour cream and season with salt and pepper. Garnish with green onion.

Fry bacon strips in another pan (or you can bake them instead).

Serve eggs with bacon strips on the side.

Each serving contains:
- ⊕ Calories: 710
- ⊕ Fats: 57 g
- ⊕ Protein: 37 g
- ⊕ Carbs: 2.5 g

26

Good Ol' Steak and Eggs

(Makes 1 serving)

Ingredients:
- ◊ 4 oz. sirloin (or any cut of steak)
- ◊ 3 large eggs
- ◊ 1 tablespoon olive oil
- ◊ 1 tablespoon butter
- ◊ ½ avocado
- ◊ Salt and pepper to taste

Instructions:

Put olive oil in pan, and cook the sirloin (or steak cut) up to desired doneness.

While the sirloin is cooking, melt butter in another pan and fry the eggs until the whites set and the yolks are cooked to desired doneness. Add a dash of salt and pepper.

Take the steak off the pan. Slice meat into bite-sized cuts. Season with salt and pepper.

Slice the avocado, and sprinkle with a little salt.

Serve everything together.

One serving contains:
- ⊕ Calories: 687 g
- ⊕ Fats: 52 g
- ⊕ Protein:43 g
- ⊕ Carbs: 5 g

- SECTION 3 -

CHICKEN

27

Lemon Rosemary Chicken

Ingredients:
- ◊ 3 1/2 Chicken Thigh, boneless and skinless
- ◊ 1 1/2 teaspoon garlic, minced
- ◊ 1 1/2 tsp. Olive Oil
- ◊ 1 Lemon
- ◊ 1 1/2 teaspoon fresh thyme
- ◊ 3/4 teaspoon dried rosemary
- ◊ 1/2 teaspoon dried ground Sage
- ◊ 1 teaspoon kosher salt

Instructions:

Place garlic and ½ teaspoon in a mortar. Grind them together with a pestle to form a paste.

Gradually add oil, grinding and mixing the paste into an aioli.

Once the aioli is done, dry the chicken off and place it inside a bag with the aioli. Coat the chicken well.

Marinate the chicken for 2-10 hours (the longer, the better).

Preheat oven to 425F.

Slice 1 lemon thin and arrange the slices on the bottom of a baking pan.

Lay the chicken on top of the lemons.

Remove the thyme leaves from the stem and add it together with the rosemary, pepper, sage, and remaining salt to the chicken.

Bake for 25 to 30 minutes, or until the juices run clear.

Remove the chicken from the pan and add all the pan drippings to a saucepan.

Bring the sauce to a boil while stirring constantly.

Turn the heat down to medium-low while continuing to stir the sauce. Allow it to reduce.

Spoon the sauce over the chicken. Serve immediately.

This dish contains:
- ⊕ Calories: 589
- ⊕ Fat: 40.5 g
- ⊕ Net carbs: 4.2 g
- ⊕ Protein: 47 g

28

Pesto Chicken Casserole with Olives and Feta Cheese

Takes 15 minutes to prepare, and 30 minutes to cook. Makes 5 servings.

Ingredients:
- ◊ 2 lbs. chicken thighs or chicken breasts
- ◊ 5 oz. red or green pesto
- ◊ 2/3 cup olives, pitted
- ◊ 2 cups heavy whipping cream
- ◊ 2/3 lb feta cheese, diced
- ◊ 1¼ garlic clove, finely chopped
- ◊ Salt and pepper to taste
- ◊ 1-2 tablespoon butter for frying

To add when serving:
- ◊ 6¼ oz. any leafy green veggies
- ◊ olive oil
- ◊ sea salt

Instructions:
Preheat the oven to 400°F.

Cut the chicken thighs or breasts into small pieces. Sprinkle with salt and pepper as seasoning, and fry in butter until golden brown.

In a bowl, combine pesto and heavy cream.

Place the fried chicken pieces in a baking dish together with olives, garlic, and feta cheese. Then add in the pesto mix.

Bake in oven for 20 to 30 minutes, until the dish turns into golden brown.

Serve with leafy greens tossed with olive oil and a dash of salt.

29

Crispy Jerk Chicken Drumsticks and Coleslaw

Homemade coleslaw and jerk chicken with a special breading made with pork rinds. Takes 15 minutes to prepare and 40 minutes to cook. Makes 4 servings.

Ingredients:
◊ 8 chicken drumsticks (with skin on)
◊ ½ cup Greek yogurt or sour cream
◊ 1/3 lb pork rinds
◊ 2 tablespoons jerk seasoning
◊ 2 tablespoons olive oil
◊ 3 oz. shredded coconut (unsweetened)
◊ ¼ cup olive oil
◊ 1 teaspoon salt

For the coleslaw:
◊ 1 lb green cabbage, shredded
◊ 1 cup mayonnaise
◊ Dash of salt and pepper

Instructions:
Preheat oven to 350°F.

Make marinade by mixing jerk seasoning, sour cream and salt.

Place drumsticks inside a big plastic bag, and then pour the marinade into the same bag. Shake well to mix. Leave for about 15 minutes to marinate.

Take out the drumsticks from the bag. Dispose of the bag and marinade.

Get a new, clean bag and put the drumsticks here.

Put the pork rinds in a blender to turn them into fine crumbs. Mix in the coconut flakes, and process for a bit longer.

Place the crumbs mixture into the bag with the drumsticks and shake briskly.

Lightly grease a baking dish, and put the drumsticks on it. Pour olive oil over the drumsticks.

Bake in oven until chicken is fully cooked; this should take a total of around 40 to 45 minutes. About halfway through (around 20 minutes), turn the drumsticks. If the breading looks "cooked" enough, reduce the heat to avoid burning the coconut flakes which are heat-sensitive.

While waiting for the chicken to fully bake, make the coleslaw. Using a sharp knife or a food processor, shred the cabbage into thin bits.

Put the cabbage in a medium bowl, then add mayonnaise, salt and pepper. Mix thoroughly and set aside for about 10 minutes.

30

Deviled Chicken Halves

(Makes 4 servings)

Ingredients:
- ◊ 1 chicken
- ◊ 1/4 cup butter
- ◊ 2 tablespoons lemon juice
- ◊ 2 tablespoons vegetable oil
- ◊ 1 teaspoon mustard
- ◊ 1/4 teaspoon cayenne pepper
- ◊ 1/4 cup green onion, minced
- ◊ 1 teaspoon garlic, minced
- ◊ Lemon wedges

Instructions:

Preheat broiler. Wash chicken and split into equal halves down at the middle. In a mixing bowl, combine oil, butter, mustard, lemon juice and cayenne pepper.

Brush chicken with the mixture.

Then add onions, salt and garlic into remaining mixture.

Place chicken in a broiler pan, skin side down. Broil for 20 minutes, flip, and broil the other side for 10 minutes.

Baste with remaining butter mixture and broil another 10 minutes until chicken is tender.

Serve with lemon wedges.

Each serving contains:

- ⊕ Net carbs: 2 grams

31

No-Guilt Chicken Quesadilla

(Makes 1 serving)

Ingredients:
- ◊ 2.5 oz. chicken breast, grilled and shredded
- ◊ 1 low-carb wrap
- ◊ 3 oz. pepper jack cheese, shredded
- ◊ ½ avocado, thinly sliced
- ◊ 1 teaspoon jalapeño, chopped
- ◊ ¼ teaspoon salt

Instructions:

Place the wrap flat open on a frying pan over medium heat.

After about 2 minutes, flip wrap over.

Place the pepper jack cheese on the wrap, but keep about an inch from the edges of the wrap empty.

After the cheese, place the chicken shreds, jalapeño and avocado on one-half of the wrap.

Fold the wrap over using a spatula or tongs, press down a bit to flatten, to help the melted cheese act as glue that keeps the quesadilla together.

Remove quesadilla from the pan and cut into thirds.

Serve with sour cream or salsa, or both.

One serving contains:
- ⊕ Calories: 654
- ⊕ Fat: 43g
- ⊕ Protein: 52
- ⊕ Carbs: 7

- SECTION 4 -

BEEF

32

Creamy-Spicy Sesame Beef

Ingredients:
- ◊ 1/2 pound 90% lean ground beef
- ◊ Taco seasoning or Mexican spices (check label for carb content)
- ◊ 2 ounces hot pepper cheese, shredded
- ◊ ½ tablespoon sesame seeds
- ◊ 1 ounce sour cream
- ◊ Water

Instructions:

Brown the ground beef in a skillet. Add one tablespoon or more of water, as needed.

Add a dash of Mexican spices or taco seasoning to taste.

Mix thoroughly and simmer for 10 to 15 minutes in a skillet.

Remove from heat and spread shredded hot pepper cheese over the beef.

Mix sesame seeds and sour cream.

Serve the spicy seasoned beef with the sour cream mixture on the side, or mix a measured amount right into the dish for a creamy texture.

This dish contains:
- ⊕ Calories: 518
- ⊕ Fat: 32g
- ⊕ Protein: 53g
- ⊕ Net Carbs: 4.5

33

Stuffed Cabbage Casserole

Easy to cook, and simply delicious. Takes 10 minutes to prepare, and 30 minutes to cook. Makes 2 servings.

Ingredients:
- ◊ ½ lb ground beef
- ◊ ¾ lb green cabbage
- ◊ 2½ oz. butter
- ◊ 1 tablespoon Tex-mex seasoning
- ◊ ½ tablespoon white wine vinegar
- ◊ ½ teaspoon salt
- ◊ ½ teaspoon onion powder
- ◊ 1/8 teaspoon ground black pepper
- ◊ 1/3 lb shredded Cheddar cheese

To add when ready to serve:
- ◊ 2 2/3 oz. lettuce or leafy greens

Instructions:

Shred the cabbage very finely, either by hand or using a food processor.

In a large pan or wok, fry shredded cabbage in butter over medium high heat. Add vinegar and spices. Stir and continue to fry for a few minutes. Remove from heat before cabbage turns brown. Then set aside in a bowl.

In the same pan, melt the remaining butter. Sauté the ground beef until almost dry. Reduce the heat a little, add the cabbage, and continue to sauté for one minute. Add salt and pepper to taste. Set aside.

Preheat the oven to 400°F. Sprinkle about ⅔ of the cheese to the cabbage and put in a baking dish.

Add the rest of the cheese on top of the cabbage, and bake for 15 to 20 minutes, or until the cheese turns into a nice color.

Serve with leafy greens or lettuce.

34

Beef Curry

Makes 4 servings

Ingredients:

◊ 1 lb beef (preferably beef round or any other boneless cut), diced into 1-inch slices
◊ 1 tablespoon fish sauce
◊ 2 garlic cloves, minced
◊ 1 tablespoon curry powder
◊ 1 teaspoon ginger, grated
◊ ¼ cup basil leaves, finely shredded
◊ ¾ cup coconut milk
◊ 1 medium onion, finely sliced
◊ Dash of salt
◊ Coconut oil (to use for cooking in)
◊ 1 teaspoon each of ground cumin, ground coriander, ground turmeric, and cardamom

Optional ingredients:

◊ 10 button mushrooms, diced
◊ 2 carrots, sliced
◊ 1 bell pepper, diced

Instructions:

Pour coconut oil in a saucepan and, over medium heat, sauté the beef and onions until the beef turns brown. This should take about 5 to 6 minutes.

Pour in the coconut milk and fish sauce, then add the spices, mushrooms, carrots and bell peppers.

Let the mixture boil. Then cover with a lid and let simmer for about an hour to thoroughly cook the beef.

Put in the garlic, basil, ginger and salt. Simmer for an additional 10 minutes.

Each serving contains:
- ⊕ Calories: 440
- ⊕ Fat: 33g
- ⊕ Carbohydrates: 11g
- ⊕ Sugar: 2g
- ⊕ Fiber: 4g
- ⊕ Protein: 25g

35

Filet Mignon with Portobello Sauce

Makes 4 servings

Ingredients:
- ◊ 4 beef tenderloin steaks
- ◊ 8 green onions, sliced into 1-inch pieces
- ◊ 2 large Portobello mushrooms, halved and sliced
- ◊ 1/3 cup reduced sodium beef broth
- ◊ 2 tablespoons Madeira or Port wine
- ◊ 1 teaspoon olive oil
- ◊ 1 teaspoon black pepper
- ◊ 1 tablespoon butter

Instructions:

Mix oil with pepper and use to baste both sides of steaks.

In a big skillet, prepare sauce as follows: heat butter over medium to high heat, then sauté onions and mushrooms until tender. Add wine and broth, and let the mixture boil. Remove from heat.

Charcoal grill the steaks as follows: Grill steaks uncovered over medium hot coals, until desired doneness is achieved. Turn steaks once halfway through grilling. When done, slice thin and cover with onion and mushroom sauté.

Each serving contains:

Total Net Carbs: 3g

36

Stir-Fried Asian Beef and Cabbage

A delicious, low-carb favorite that's also called crack slaw. Makes 2 servings.

Ingredients:
- ◊ 2/3 lb ground beef
- ◊ ¾ lb green cabbage
- ◊ 2½ oz. butter
- ◊ 1 garlic clove
- ◊ ½ teaspoon salt
- ◊ ½ teaspoon onion powder
- ◊ ½ tablespoon white wine vinegar
- ◊ 1/8 teaspoon ground black pepper
- ◊ 1½ scallion, sliced
- ◊ ½ teaspoon chili flakes
- ◊ ½ tablespoon fresh ginger, grated or very finely chopped
- ◊ ½ tablespoon sesame oil
- ◊ ½ cup mayonnaise
- ◊ ¼ - ½ tablespoon wasabi paste

Instructions:

Shred the cabbage finely with a sharp knife or using a food processor.

Fry the cabbage in butter in a large pan or wok on medium high, taking care not to let the cabbage turn brown. Add vinegar and spices, and stir-fry for a few more minutes. Put the cooked cabbage in a bowl.

Melt the remaining butter in the same frying pan. Add garlic, ginger and chili flakes, and sauté for a few minutes. Then add ground meat, and brown until meat is cooked and almost dry.

Reduce the heat a bit. Add cabbage and scallions. Stir until all ingredients are cooked well. Season with salt and pepper, and add sesame oil as final touch.

Blend together a little wasabi paste and mayonnaise, gradually adding more wasabi until the desired taste is achieved.

Serve the stir-fried beef cabbage with a dollop of wasabi mayonnaise on top.

Variation:

Cook this dish with other ground meat such as pork, poultry or lamb.

- SECTION 5 -

PORK

37

Lemon Marinated Sirloin

Makes 6 servings.

Ingredients:
- ◊ 1 pound steak (any cut)
- ◊ 1 teaspoon finely shredded lemon peel
- ◊ 1/2 cup lemon juice
- ◊ 1/3 cup cooking oil
- ◊ 2 tablespoons sliced green onion
- ◊ 4 teaspoons Splenda
- ◊ 1 1/2 teaspoons salt
- ◊ 1 teaspoon Worcestershire sauce
- ◊ 1 teaspoon prepared mustard
- ◊ 1/8 teaspoon pepper

Instructions:

If steak has fat around edges, be sure to score them first with a knife.

Place the steak into a shallow baking dish.

Combine all ingredients to make the lemon marinade and pour over steak. Allow to sit in the refrigerator for at least 4 hours so the marinade has a chance to soak in.

Grill steak to your preference on an outdoor grill, adding leftover marinade during cooking to maintain tenderness.

One serving contains:

Total Net carbs: 2g

38

Broccoli and Cauliflower Gratin with Sausage

A very tasty dish that could become your favorite once you've tried it. Best cooked using high-quality sausages. Takes about 5 minutes to prepare, and 30 minutes to cook. Makes 4 servings.

Ingredients:
- ◊ 1 lb sausages
- ◊ 1 lb broccoli florets
- ◊ ½ lb cauliflower florets
- ◊ 1 leek
- ◊ 1 yellow onion, chopped
- ◊ 2 tablespoons Dijon mustard
- ◊ 1 cup sour cream
- ◊ 4 oz. cheese, shredded
- ◊ 2 oz. butter, to use for frying
- ◊ ¼ cup fresh thyme
- ◊ A dash of salt and pepper

Instructions:

Preheat the oven to 450°F.

Chop sausages and vegetables.

Fry the sausages in butter in a pan, and the onion and vegetables (also in butter) in a different pan. Put the vegetables in a baking dish.

Blend the mustard and sour cream, and pour the mixture over the vegetables.

Put the sausages and cheese on top of the vegetables. Add thyme.

Bake on upper rack of oven for about 15 minutes.

39

Bacon Wrapped Pork Tenderloin

Ingredients:
- ◊ 1/2 lb. pork tenderloin
- ◊ 2 1/2 slices bacon
- ◊ 1 1/2 teaspoon Dijon Mustard
- ◊ 1 1/2 teaspoon sugar-free maple syrup
- ◊ 3/4 teaspoon soy sauce
- ◊ 1/4 teaspoon garlic, minced
- ◊ 1/4 teaspoon liquid smoke
- ◊ 1/4 teaspoon dried rosemary
- ◊ A dash of black pepper, cayenne and dried sage

Instructions:

To make the marinade, mix together all the wet and dry ingredients

Pat the pork tenderloins dry with a paper towel and put them in a Ziploc bag.

Pour marinade into the bag and rub onto the tenderloins. Place this in the refrigerator for 3 to 5 hours.

Preheat oven to 350F.

Wrap pork tenderloins in the bacon slices, and place on a foil baking sheet.

Bake for 1 hour, and then broil the bacon for 5-10 minutes.

Cover the tenderloins with foil for 10-15 minutes to cool.

Cut and serve.

The whole dish contains:
- ⊕ Calories: 418
- ⊕ Fat: 20g
- ⊕ Protein: 54g
- ⊕ Net Carbs: 0.3g

40

Ham and Cheddar Wraps

Ingredients:
- ◊ 1 low-carb wrap
- ◊ 2 oz. deli ham
- ◊ 2 oz. cheddar, shredded
- ◊ 2 tablespoon mayonnaise
- ◊ Jalapenos or pickles to taste (optional)
- ◊ Salt and pepper

Instructions:

Spread the mayonnaise on the low-carb wrap.

Add the ham slices and cheese.

Add some pickles or jalapenos to liven up the taste and texture.

Wrap tight and cut it to any desired length.

One serving contains:
- ⊕ Calories: 600
- ⊕ Fat: 44g
- ⊕ Protein: 27g
- ⊕ Carbs: 8g

- SECTION 6 -

FISH

41

Thai Fish with Curry and Coconut

A simple, tasty Asian-inspired dish. Takes 10 minutes to prepare, and 20 minutes to cook. Makes 5 servings.

Ingredients:
- ◊ 2 lbs salmon or white fish
- ◊ Salt and pepper to season
- ◊ 5 tablespoons ghee or butter
- ◊ 1¼ - 2½ tablespoons red or green curry paste
- ◊ 1¼ cans coconut cream
- ◊ 2/3 cup fresh cilantro, chopped
- ◊ Olive oil or butter to grease the baking dish

Instructions:

Preheat the oven to 400°F.

Grease a deep, medium-sized baking dish, and put in the fish pieces. (Choose a dish that is just big enough to accommodate the fish.)

Add salt and pepper to the fish. Then put a tablespoon of butter on each fish piece.

In a small bowl, mix coconut cream, curry paste and cilantro. Spread this mixture over the fish.

Bake in oven until the fish is done (should take about 20 minutes).

Serve immediately

Variations:

Use 2 cans of coconut milk if coconut cream isn't available. First refrigerate the unopened cans overnight, then open and remove the coconut water.

This dish may be served with boiled vegetables (broccoli or cauliflower is best) or with cooked rice and vegetables.

Each serving contains:
- ⊕ Carbs: 5g

42

Sunflower Butter Salmon with Onions

Ingredients:
- ◊ 4 ounces salmon fillet
- ◊ ½ onion, sliced
- ◊ 1-2 tablespoon olive oil
- ◊ 1 tablespoon sunflower seed butter
- ◊ 1/4 teaspoon lemon juice
- ◊ ½ cup spinach, broccoli or any other low-carb vegetable

Instructions:

Grill the salmon fillet to desired texture.

Cook the onion pieces in a hot skillet with olive oil until their color becomes golden-brown caramel.

Remove the onions from heat and set on the plate.

Mix sunflower seed butter and lemon juice and heat in the skillet, stirring continually.

Rest the salmon on a small pile of spinach or broccoli.

Pour sunflower butter sauce over the salmon and vegetables.

Serve while hot.

This dish contains:
- ⊕ Calories: 490
- ⊕ Fat: 31g
- ⊕ Protein: 44g
- ⊕ Net Carbs: 6

43

Dinner Dill Trout

(Makes 6 servings)

Ingredients:
- ◊ 2 pounds dressed trout, fresh or frozen (leave skin on)
- ◊ 1/2 cup margarine or butter
- ◊ 1 1/2 teaspoon salt
- ◊ 1/4 teaspoon pepper
- ◊ 3 tablespoons lemon juice
- ◊ 2 tablespoons dill weed

Instructions:

Cut fish lengthwise, spread open and season with salt and pepper.

Prepare a fry pan with melted butter and dill weed.

Put fish in pan, flesh side down, and fry for 2 to 3 minutes. Flip over, and fry for another 2-3 minutes on other side.

Remove fish.

Add lemon juice to butter and dill, and use this as sauce for garnishing.

One serving contains:

Net carbs: 1 gram

44

Creamy Fish and Broccoli Casserole

An easy-to-make dish good for entertaining or eating alone. Takes 10 minutes to prepare and about 30 minutes to cook. Makes 2 servings.

Ingredients:
- ◊ ¾ lb white fish, cut in small pieces
- ◊ 1 tablespoon olive oil
- ◊ 2/3 cup heavy whipping cream
- ◊ 3 scallions, finely chopped
- ◊ 1 tablespoon small capers
- ◊ ½ lb broccoli
- ◊ ½ ounce butter (to grease the casserole dish)
- ◊ ½ tablespoon Dijon mustard
- ◊ ½ teaspoon salt
- ◊ ½ tablespoon dried parsley
- ◊ 1/8 teaspoon ground black pepper
- ◊ 1½ ounce butter

Instructions:
Preheat the oven to 400°F.

Divide the broccoli into small florets; also cut the stems. Fry for about 5 minutes until soft and golden. Then add the scallions, capers, salt and pepper. Fry for 1 to 2 more minutes. Next, transfer the fried vegetables in a greased baking dish.

Place the fish in between the vegetables.

Mix parsley, mustard and whipping cream, and pour over the fish and vegetables. Top with slices of butter.

Bake in the oven until fish is cooked; this should take about 20-30 minutes minutes.

Variations:

Instead of white fish, you can use salmon or tuna (fresh or frozen).

In place of broccoli, you can also use asparagus, Brussel sprouts, mushrooms or zucchini.

45

Garlic Ghee Pan-Fried Cod

(Makes 4 servings)

Ingredients:
- ◊ 4 cod fillet slices (about 0.3 lb each)
- ◊ 6 cloves of garlic, minced
- ◊ 3 tablespoon ghee
- ◊ 1 tablespoon garlic powder (optional)
- ◊ Dash of salt

Instructions:

Melt ghee in a frying pan. Place half of the garlic into the pan, followed by the cod fillets. Cook on medium to high heat.

Sprinkle with salt and garlic powder.

When the color of the fish fillet turns to solid white half-way up the side of the fish, flip it. Add the remaining minced garlic.

Cook until the whole fish turns a solid white color; it should also flake easily by this time.

Serve with some of the ghee and garlic from the pan.

The whole dish contains:
- ⊕ Calories: 160
- ⊕ Fat: 7g
- ⊕ Carbohydrates: 1g
- ⊕ Protein: 21 g

46

Baked Salmon with Lemon and Butter

Great for dinner with family or friends. Takes 10 minutes to prepare and 25 minutes to cook. Makes 6 servings.

Ingredients:
- ◊ 2 – 3 lbs salmon
- ◊ 1 tablespoon olive oil
- ◊ 1 teaspoon sea salt
- ◊ 7 oz. butter
- ◊ 1 lemon
- ◊ Ground black pepper

Instructions:
Preheat the oven to 400°F.

Grease a baking dish with olive oil, and place in it the salmon, with the skin down. Rub salt and pepper on the fish generously.

Slice the lemon thinly and put on top of the salmon. Use half of the butter, also thinly sliced, to cover the salmon.

Bake on middle rack for about 20 to 30 minutes. (A bigger fish needs longer baking time.)

Put the rest of the butter in a small saucepan and heat briefly. Remove from heat when the butter starts to bubble, and let it cool for about 2 minutes. Add lemon juice.

Serve fish with the lemon butter.

Each serving contains:

- ⊕ 1 g carbs

47

Shrimp with Garlic Sauce

Takes 5 minutes to prepare, and 5 minutes to cook. Makes 2 servings.

Ingredients:
- ◊ 1/2 lb large shrimp
- ◊ 3 cloves garlic, minced
- ◊ 1/4 cup olive oil
- ◊ 1/4 tsp cayenne
- ◊ 1 wedge lemon
- ◊ Salt and pepper to taste

Instructions:

In a small pan, pour olive oil and then add garlic and cayenne. Cook over medium-low heat until it becomes fragrant.

Peel and devein the shrimp (as necessary). Cook for 2 to 3 minutes on each side.

Add salt and pepper, and squeeze the lemon wedge over the shrimp.

Serve warm. The remaining garlic oil may be served on the side as a dipping sauce.

Each serving contains:
- ⊕ Calories: 335 Calories
- ⊕ Fat: 27g
- ⊕ Protein: 22.3g
- ⊕ Net Carbs: 2.5g

48

Salmon Sushi Mousse

A really easy snack for sushi lovers. Takes only 8 minutes to prepare, no cooking needed. Makes 6 servings.

Ingredients:
- ◊ 2 ounces smoked salmon, roughly chopped
- ◊ 2 ounces cream cheese
- ◊ 2 teaspoons wasabi paste
- ◊ 1 teaspoon coconut aminos
- ◊ 6 seaweed snack sheets

Instructions:

In a small food processor, place smoked salmon, cream cheese, wasabi, and coconut aminos; blend well to form a smooth cream.

Place 1 tablespoon of this mixture on each seaweed snack sheet. Roll to make one serving. Serve immediately.

One serving contains:
- ⊕ Calories: 50
- ⊕ Fat: 4g
- ⊕ Protein: 3g
- ⊕ Sodium: 186mg
- ⊕ Carbohydrates: 2g

49

Sesame Salmon Burgers

(Makes 12 burgers)

Ingredients:
- ◊ 1 pound salmon (skinless)
- ◊ 2 large eggs
- ◊ 1 tablespoon toasted sesame oil
- ◊ 1 tablespoon vinegar
- ◊ 1 clove garlic, pressed
- ◊ 1 teaspoon ginger, fresh, peeled and minced
- ◊ ¼ cup scallions, chopped
- ◊ ¼ cup toasted sesame seeds
- ◊ 1 tablespoon coconut flour
- ◊ coconut oil, to use for frying

Instructions:

Rinse the salmon, pat dry with paper towel, and cut into cubes (about ¼-inch size)

Combine eggs, salmon, oil, vinegar, garlic, ginger, scallions and sesame seeds in a large bowl. Slowly add in the coconut flour while stirring.

Form mixture into patties using a ¼-cup measuring cup.

Heat the coconut oil in a medium skillet over medium heat. Fry the patties for 4 to 6 minutes on each side, until they turn into a nice golden brown color.

Place patties on a paper towel to remove excess moisture.

Transfer to a plate and serve hot.

- SECTION 7 -

SALADS

50

Cauliflower Tabouli Salad

(Makes 2 servings)

Ingredients:

- ◊ 100 g cauliflower florets
- ◊ 3 mint leaves, finely diced
- ◊ 2 cherry tomatoes, diced
- ◊ 2 tablespoons parsley, finely diced
- ◊ 1 slice lemon, diced
- ◊ 1 tablespoon olive oil
- ◊ Salt
- ◊ Pepper

Instructions:

In a small food processor, pulse the cauliflower florets to form a mixture with granulated texture (not a mash). The way to do this is to check first that there is no moisture in either the florets or the food processor.

Combine the food-processed cauliflower florets with the diced herbs, tomatoes, olive oil, lemon slice. Add salt and pepper to taste.

Each serving contains:

- ⊕ Calories: 80
- ⊕ Fat: 7 g
- ⊕ Carbohydrates: 5 g
- ⊕ Sugar: 2 g
- ⊕ Fiber: 2 g
- ⊕ Protein: 1 g

51

Broccoli Bacon Salad with Onions and Coconut Cream

(Makes 6 servings)

Ingredients:
- ◊ 1 lb broccoli florets
- ◊ 2 large red onions (or 4 small ones), sliced
- ◊ 20 slices of bacon, chopped into small pieces
- ◊ 1 cup coconut cream
- ◊ Dash of salt

Instructions:

Cook the bacon. Set aside.

Next, cook the onions in the bacon fat.

Blanch the broccoli florets by scalding them in boiling water and then removing them from the water after 2-3 minutes. Rinse in tap water to cool.

Toss the bacon pieces, broccoli florets and onions together with the coconut cream, and add salt to taste.

Each serving contains:
- ⊕ Calories: 280
- ⊕ Fat: 26 g
- ⊕ Carbohydrates: 8 g
- ⊕ Sugar: 2 g
- ⊕ Fiber: 3 g
- ⊕ Protein: 7 g

52

Quick Lunch Salad

Ingredients:
- ◊ 2 to 4 tablespoon olive oil
- ◊ 2 cups spinach
- ◊ 1-2 tablespoon Parmesan cheese
- ◊ 1 1/2 teaspoon Dijon Mustard
- ◊ ¾ teaspoon curry powder (optional)
- ◊ ¼ teaspoon lemon zest
- ◊ Any cooked meat, diced or sliced (leftovers are fine)

Instructions:

Combine all wet ingredients in a small bowl.

Combine spinach and meat in a bowl.

Pour wet ingredients over meat and spinach, and serve immediately.

Nutritional contents are variable, depending on what meat was used.

53

Potato-Less Potato Salad

(Makes 2-3 servings)

Ingredients:
- ◊ 2 large hard-boiled eggs, diced
- ◊ 1 head cauliflower
- ◊ 2 stalks celery, diced
- ◊ 1 small onion, finely chopped (should make about 3-4 tablespoons)
- ◊ 2 tablespoons Primal Kitchen mayo
- ◊ 1 tablespoons parsley, finely chopped
- ◊ 1 tablespoon Dijon mustard
- ◊ ½ teaspoon sea salt

Instructions:

Slice cauliflower into small florets (about a half inch each).

Steam cauliflower on the stove until tender (test with a fork to check).

Let the cauliflower slices cool, then place in a large bowl.

Add eggs, onion, celery, and parsley.

Mix in the mayonnaise, mustard and salt.

54

Tuna Avocado Salad

Ingredients:
- ◊ 4 oz. canned tuna
- ◊ 1 hard-boiled egg, peeled and chopped
- ◊ ½ stalk celery, diced
- ◊ ½ avocado
- ◊ 2 tablespoon mayonnaise
- ◊ 1 teaspoon mustard
- ◊ ½ teaspoon fresh lemon juice
- ◊ Salt and pepper to taste

Instructions:

Combine the tuna, avocado and celery in a bowl. Add mustard, mayonnaise, lemon juice and spices.

Add the egg to the tuna salad. Mix all ingredients well.

Serve right away, or cool in the fridge first.

One serving contains:
- ⊕ Calories: 508
- ⊕ Fat: 34g
- ⊕ Protein: 31g
- ⊕ Carbs: 5g

55

Simple Cucumber Salad

(Makes 6 servings)

Ingredients:
- ◊ 2 cucumbers, thinly sliced
- ◊ 4 green onions, thinly sliced
- ◊ 3 small tomatoes
- ◊ 2 tablespoons snipped parsley
- ◊ 1/4 cup sour cream
- ◊ 1/4 Teaspoon mustard
- ◊ 2 Tablespoons minced dill
- ◊ 1 Tablespoon vinegar
- ◊ 1 Tablespoon heavy cream
- ◊ 1/2 Teaspoon salt
- ◊ 1/2 Teaspoon pepper

Instructions:

Dice and combine cucumbers, tomatoes, onions, and parsley.

Mix dressing ingredients, then pour over salad. Toss lightly.

Chill 1-2 hours and then serve.

Each serving contains:
- ⊕ Total Net carbs: 9 grams

56

No-Fuss Cobb Salad

(Makes 1 serving)

Ingredients
- ◊ 4 oz. chicken breast
- ◊ 1 cup spinach
- ◊ 1 large hard-boiled egg
- ◊ 2 strips bacon
- ◊ ¼ avocado
- ◊ 1 tablespoon olive oil
- ◊ ½ teaspoon white vinegar

Instructions:
Cook egg for about 10 minutes in a pot of boiling water. Cool in cold water and chop into slices.

On a frying pan, cook chicken breast and bacon to desired crispiness. Shred or chop spinach leaves and add in with the bacon and chicken. Also add chopped egg.

Add avocado and mix with everything to mash it up.

Dress with olive oil and vinegar. (Alternatively, you can use a low carb Bleu cheese dressing instead.)

A serving contains:
- ⊕ Calories: 600
- ⊕ Fats: 48g
- ⊕ Protein: 43g
- ⊕ Carbs: 2g

- SECTION 8 -

DESSERTS

57

Sour Cream and Rosemary Panna Cotta

An easy, savory recipe using everyday ingredients. Takes 6-12 hours to prepare, and 7 minutes to cook. Makes 6 servings.

Ingredients:

◊ 1 1/2 cups heavy whipping cream
◊ 1 1/2 cups sour cream
◊ 2 medium sprigs fresh rosemary, plus extra leaves for garnish
◊ 2 teaspoons powdered gelatin (unflavored)
◊ 1 teaspoon sea salt

Instructions:

In a small saucepan, combine heavy cream, sour cream, and rosemary sprigs and cook over medium heat. Stir until they melt together.

Whisk in gelatin and salt until thoroughly blended.

For about 4 minutes, simmer at very low heat, stirring constantly.

Remove rosemary sprigs from cream.

Pour mixture evenly into 6 small glasses or ramekins.

Refrigerate until set, overnight or at for least 6 hours.

Decorate each glass with a few rosemary leaves.

Each serving contains:
- ⊕ Calories: 332
- ⊕ Fat: 34g
- ⊕ Protein: 3g
- ⊕ Sodium: 466mg
- ⊕ Fiber: 1g
- ⊕ Carbohydrates: 5g
- ⊕ Sugar: 2g

58

Creamy Lemon Bars

Great as snack or dessert, and as energy bar when working out. Takes 30 minutes to prepare, no cooking needed. Makes 8 bars.

Ingredients:
- ◊ 1 cup pecan pieces
- ◊ 4 ounces butter, melted
- ◊ 3 ounces powdered gelatin (unflavored)
- ◊ 1/4 cup coconut flour
- ◊ 8 ounces cream cheese, softened
- ◊ 2 tablespoons fresh lemon juice
- ◊ 1 tablespoon lemon zest
- ◊ 1/4 cup granular Swerve
- ◊ 1 cup boiling water
- ◊ **Instructions:**

In a small bowl, combine pecan pieces, coconut flour and melted butter. Spread mixture into an 8" × 8" silicone or glass baking dish and set aside.

Place gelatin in boiling water in a medium bowl, and stir for about 2 minutes.

Add remaining ingredients to this bowl and mix thoroughly until all lumps disappear.

Pour mixture over pecan crust and place in refrigerator to set.

Cut into 8 bars and serve chilled.

Each bar contains:

- ⊕ Calories: 333
- ⊕ Fat: 31g
- ⊕ Protein: 13g
- ⊕ Sodium: 114mg
- ⊕ Fiber: 4g
- ⊕ Carbohydrates: 6g
- ⊕ Sugar: 2g

59

Dark Chocolate Orange Truffles

A delicious Martinique treat that combines orange and dark chocolate. Takes 1 hour and 15 minutes to prepare, plus 10 minutes cooking time. Makes 9 servings.

Ingredients:

Ganache:

◊ 3 ounces unsweetened baking chocolate
◊ 2 tablespoons confectioners Swerve
◊ 2 tablespoons heavy cream
◊ 1 tablespoon butter
◊ 2 drops stevia glycerite
◊ 1/2 teaspoon liquid orange flavor

Coating:

◊ 1 teaspoon confectioners Swerve
◊ 2 teaspoons unsweetened cocoa powder
◊ 1 teaspoon fresh orange zest

Instructions:

Melt chocolate in a small double boiler (bain-marie) over medium heat, while slowly stirring.

Add cream, Swerve, butter, stevia and orange flavor to chocolate. Mix well until blended.

Remove from heat and continue stirring for about 10 seconds.

Place saucepan in refrigerator for about one hour until ganache has congealed.

Scoop ganache with a spoon and form 9 small balls. (Tip: Wear plastic gloves while doing this so that the chocolate will not stick to your hands.)

To make coating, mix cocoa powder, confectioners Swerve and orange zest on a plate.

Roll ganache balls through coating powder until thinly coated.

For best consistency, keep refrigerated if room temperature exceeds 70°F.

Each ball contains:
- ⊕ Calories: 78
- ⊕ Fat: 7g
- ⊕ Protein: 1g
- ⊕ Sodium: 4mg
- ⊕ Fiber: 2g
- ⊕ Carbohydrates: 5g
- ⊕ Sugar: 2g

60

Gorgonzola Panna Cotta

A delicious and fancy-looking panna cotta that's surprisingly easy to make. Takes 6-12 hours to prepare, and 5 minutes to cook. Makes 6 servings.

Ingredients
- ◊ 12 ounces crumbled blue cheese or Gorgonzola
- ◊ 1 1/2 cups heavy whipping cream
- ◊ 2 teaspoons powdered unflavored gelatin
- ◊ 12 pecan halves

Instructions:

Use a small saucepan to melt Gorgonzola in heavy cream over medium heat, for about 2 minutes. Use a whisk to remove clots.

Whisk in gelatin until completely blended.

Pour mixture evenly into 6 small ramekins or glasses.

Refrigerate until set, overnight or for at least 6 hours.

Decorate each glass with 2 pecan halves and serve.

Each serving contains:
- ⊕ Calories: 435
- ⊕ Fat: 41g
- ⊕ Protein: 14g
- ⊕ Sodium: 1,037mg
- ⊕ Carbohydrates: 3g

61

Pumpkin Pie Mousse

A sugar-free version of the beloved homey favorite. Takes 15 minutes to prepare, makes 3 servings.

Ingredients:
- ◊ 1/2 cup heavy cream
- ◊ 4 ounces canned pumpkin purée
- ◊ 4 ounces softened cream cheese
- ◊ 1/2 teaspoon pumpkin pie spice
- ◊ 8 drops liquid stevia
- ◊ 1/2 teaspoon vanilla extract
- ◊ 1/2 teaspoon cinnamon (to be used as topping)

Instructions:

In a small mixing bowl, mix heavy cream using a hand blender on high until stiff peaks form.

In another bowl, combine cream cheese and pumpkin with a hand blender until smooth. Add pumpkin pie spice, vanilla and stevia, and blend until well mixed.

Fold whipped cream into cheese mixture until incorporated.

Place mousse into 3 serving dishes. Sprinkle cinnamon on top.

Serve immediately or cover and refrigerate until ready to serve.

One serving contains:
- ⊕ Calories: 281
- ⊕ Fat: 28g
- ⊕ Protein: 3g
- ⊕ Sodium: 137mg
- ⊕ Fiber: 1g
- ⊕ Carbohydrates: 6g
- ⊕ Sugar: 3g

62

Goat Cheese and Herbs Panna Cotta

Take the fancy flavor of herbed goat cheese right into your home with this easy recipe. Takes 6 to 12 hours to prepare, and 10 minutes to cook. Makes 6 servings.

Ingredients

◊ 1 1/2 cups heavy whipping cream
◊ 3/4 cup sour cream
◊ 6 ounces soft goat cheese
◊ 2 teaspoons powdered gelatin (unflavored)
◊ 1 teaspoon Herbes de Provence
◊ 1 teaspoon sea salt

Instructions:

In a small saucepan, combine heavy cream, goat cheese, sour cream, and Herbes de Provence. Cook over medium heat, stirring until cheese melts.

Whisk in gelatin and salt until completely mixed.

Simmer on very low heat for about 5 minutes, again with constant stirring.

Pour mixture evenly into 6 small ramekins or glasses.

Refrigerate until set, overnight or for at least 6 hours.

Serve in glass. Alternatively, dip glass for a few seconds in warm water to loosen panna cotta, and then invert over a small plate.

Each serving contains:
- ⊕ Calories: 397
- ⊕ Fat: 38g
- ⊕ Protein: 11g
- ⊕ Sodium: 537mg
- ⊕ Fiber: 0g
- ⊕ Carbohydrates: 3g
- ⊕ Sugar: 2g

63

Blueberry Coconut Cream Bars

Another flavorful bar that tastes like cheesecake. Takes 2 hours to prepare, and 5 minutes to cook. Makes 20 bars.

Ingredients:

◊ 1 cup fresh blueberries
◊ 3/4 cup coconut oil
◊ 8 ounces butter
◊ 4 ounces cream cheese, softened
◊ 1/4 cup granular Swerve
◊ 1/4 cup coconut cream

Instructions:

Slightly crush the blueberries in a small bowl. Then pour them into an 8" × 8" silicone or glass baking dish.

In a medium saucepan, over medium heat, melt butter and coconut oil. Remove from heat and allow to cool for about 5 minutes.

Add remaining ingredients to saucepan and combine thoroughly with a wooden spoon.

Pour mixture over blueberries and place in freezer to set.

Remove from freezer and allow to warm up for about 15 minutes. Then cut into 20 equal-sized servings.

One bar contains:

- ⊕ Calories: 189
- ⊕ Fat: 20g
- ⊕ Protein: 1g
- ⊕ Sodium: 21mg
- ⊕ Carbohydrates: 3g
- ⊕ Sugar: 3g

64

Turmeric-Infused Panna Cotta

The exotic turmeric isn't normally used to make dessert, but here it makes perfect sense. Or perfect taste, shall we say? This takes 6-12 hours to prepare, and 8 minutes to cook. Makes 6 servings.

Ingredients:
- ◊ 1 1/2 cups coconut milk, refrigerated and cream separated from the water
- ◊ 1 1/2 cups homemade beef stock
- ◊ 1 1/2 tablespoons powdered gelatin (unflavored)
- ◊ 1 tablespoon turmeric
- ◊ 1/2 tablespoon sea salt

Instructions:

In a small saucepan, heat coconut cream and beef stock on medium heat.

Whisk in gelatin until completely mixed.

Add turmeric and salt, then simmer for 5 minutes.

Pour mixture evenly into 6 small ramekins or glasses.

Refrigerate until set, overnight or for at least 6 hours.

Serve cold.

One serving contains:
- ⊕ Calories: 130
- ⊕ Fat: 12g
- ⊕ Protein: 4g
- ⊕ Sodium: 719mg
- ⊕ Fiber: 0g
- ⊕ Carbohydrates: 3g
- ⊕ Sugar: 0g

65

Coconut Custard

A dairy-free variation of the well-loved custard. Takes 4 hours, 15 minutes to prepare, and 50 minutes to cook. Makes 2 servings.

Ingredients:
- ◊ 1 cup coconut cream
- ◊ 1 large egg
- ◊ 1 large egg yolk
- ◊ 1/2 cup sweetener (erythritol or granular Swerve)
- ◊ 1/2 teaspoon vanilla extract
- ◊ 1/2 teaspoon rum extract (optional)

Instructions:

Preheat oven to 300°F.

Place 2 ramekins in a deep baking pan.

In a small saucepan over low heat, bring coconut cream to a simmer.

In a small bowl, whisk together remaining ingredients until eggs become foamy and sweetener is dissolved.

Slowly pour egg mixture into coconut cream, whisking constantly to blend well.

Pour mixture through a fine strainer into ramekins (use a spoon if needed).

Pour hot water into baking pan halfway on the ramekins.

Bake for about 35 minutes until custard is set.

Remove from oven and let cool in baking pan, for about 4 hours.

The custard can be stored in the fridge for up to 3 days.

Each serving contains:
- ⊕ Calories: 594
- ⊕ Fat: 28g
- ⊕ Protein: 6g
- ⊕ Sodium: 92mg
- ⊕ Fiber: 0g
- ⊕ Carbohydrates: 127g
- ⊕ Sugar: 77g

66

Cheesy Muffin Prosciutto Cup

Salty, creamy and nourishing—makes for a great snack or dessert. Takes 20 minutes to prepare and 12 minutes to cook. Makes 1 serving.

Ingredients
- ◊ 1 slice prosciutto (about 1/2 ounce)
- ◊ 1 medium egg yolk
- ◊ 1/2 ounce diced Brie
- ◊ 1/3 ounce diced mozzarella
- ◊ 1/2 ounce grated Parmesan

Instructions:
Preheat oven to 350°F.

Use a muffin tin with holes about 21/2" wide and 11/2" deep.

Fold prosciutto slice in half so it becomes almost square.

Place it in muffin tin hole to line it completely.

Place egg yolk into prosciutto cup.

Add cheeses on top of egg yolk gently without breaking it.

Bake for about 12 minutes until yolk is cooked and warm but still runny.

Let cool 10 minutes before removing from muffin pan.

One serving contains:

- ⊕ Calories: 218
- ⊕ Fat: 15g
- ⊕ Protein: 18g
- ⊕ Sodium: 655mg
- ⊕ Carbohydrates: 2g

67

Chocolate Chia Pudding

Who says Keto can't be sweet and chocolatey? This treat takes 20 minutes to prepare, no cooking needed. Makes 4 servings.

Ingredients:
- ◊ 1 cup heavy cream
- ◊ 1/4 cup chia seeds
- ◊ 2 tablespoons cocoa powder
- ◊ 2 tablespoons erythritol or granular Swerve
- ◊ 1 tablespoon sugar-free chocolate chips

Instructions:

In a medium bowl, mix all ingredients except chocolate chips. Allow to sit afterwards, for at least 15 minutes, stirring from time to time.

Divide among 4 cups and garnish with chocolate chips.

Serve cold. May be stored in the refrigerator up to 3 days.

One serving contains:
- ⊕ Calories: 277
- ⊕ Fat: 27g
- ⊕ Protein: 3g
- ⊕ Sodium: 26mg
- ⊕ Fiber: 3g
- ⊕ Carbohydrates: 14g
- ⊕ Sugar: 2g

68

Salty Peanut Butter Cup Fudge

Dairy-free fudge, with a bit of saltiness, to satisfy your sweet tooth without any guilt. Takes 2 hours and 5 minutes to prepare, and about 8 minutes to cook. Makes 12 servings.

Ingredients:

◊ 1/2 cup almond butter
◊ 1/2 cup coconut oil
◊ 12 drops liquid stevia
◊ 3 tablespoons cocoa powder
◊ 1 tablespoon vanilla extract
◊ 1 teaspoon coarse sea salt

Instructions:

Place a small saucepan over medium heat. Put in almond butter and coconut oil, and melt. When melted, add cocoa powder, stevia and vanilla; stir to blend well.

Pour mixture into 12 slots in a silicone candy mold or silicone-bottomed ice cube tray.

Sprinkle coarse sea salt on top of each mold.

Refrigerate for at least 2 hours until set.

One serving contains:
- ⊕ Calories: 150
- ⊕ Fat: 15g
- ⊕ Protein: 3g
- ⊕ Sodium: 246mg
- ⊕ Fiber: 1g
- ⊕ Carbohydrates: 3g
- ⊕ Sugar: 1g

- SECTION 9 -

DRINKS AND SMOOTHIES

69

Eggnog Smoothie

Delicious and filling. Takes 10 minutes to prepare, makes 2 glasses.

Ingredients:
- 8 ounces heavy cream
- 2 large eggs (separate whites from the yolks)
- 1/2 teaspoon vanilla extract
- 1 teaspoon nutmeg
- 3/8 teaspoon cinnamon, divided
- 1/8 teaspoon ground cloves
- 2 tablespoons granular Swerve
- 8 drops liquid stevia
- 8 ice cubes

Instructions:

In a medium bowl, beat egg whites using a hand mixer until firm peaks form. Set aside.

In another bowl, beat yolks with mixer until color becomes pale yellow.

Add cream, vanilla, cloves, nutmeg, 1/8 teaspoon cinnamon, stevia, and Swerve. Stir to combine.

Fold whites into yolk mixture.

Pour mix in a blender, add ice cubes, and blend until mixture becomes thick.

Pour into two glasses. On top of each glass, sprinkle 1/8 teaspoon cinnamon.

Serve and enjoy.

One glass contains:
- ⊕ Calories: 468
- ⊕ Fat: 47g
- ⊕ Protein: 9g
- ⊕ Sodium: 113mg
- ⊕ Fiber: 1g
- ⊕ Carbohydrates: 5g
- ⊕ Sugar: 1g

70

Creamy Coconut Smoothie

This delicious dairy-free drink is as tropical as anything can get. For added punch, you can put in a splash of rum extract and a pineapple wedge. It takes about 5 minutes to prepare, with no cooking involved. This makes one glass.

Ingredients
- ◊ 1/2 (13.5-ounce) can coconut milk
- ◊ 1 tablespoon powdered unflavored gelatin
- ◊ 1 tablespoon coconut oil, softened but not melted
- ◊ 1 teaspoon vanilla extract
- ◊ 1 tablespoon unsweetened shredded coconut
- ◊ 6 drops liquid stevia
- ◊ 6 ice cubes

Instructions:

Pour milk and gelatin into a blender and mix for about a minute. Add remaining ingredients except ice cubes and blend for another minute. Pour in the ice cubes into the blender and process until smoothie thickens. Serve immediately.

A glass contains:

- ⊕ Calories: 559
- ⊕ Fat: 57g
- ⊕ Protein: 10g
- ⊕ Sodium: 41mg
- ⊕ Fiber: 0g
- ⊕ Carbohydrates: 7g
- ⊕ Sugar: 1g

71

Coconut Coffee

A delicious coffee drink to start your day. It only takes about a minute to prepare.

Ingredients:
- ◊ 11/2 cups hot brewed coffee
- ◊ 2 drops of Stevia sweetener, or 2 teaspoon granular Swerve
- ◊ 1 tablespoon coconut oil
- ◊ 1 tablespoon butter
- ◊ 1/8 teaspoon sea salt

Instructions:

Put all ingredients in a blender. Blend for about 15 seconds at a high setting. Serve immediately.

This coffee contains:
- ⊕ Calories: 534
- ⊕ Carbohydrates: 61g
- ⊕ Fat: 28g
- ⊕ Protein: 16g
- ⊕ Sodium: 344mg

72

Key Lime Pie Smoothie

A tarty yet sweet tropical smoothie. Takes only 5 minutes to prepare, no cooking needed. Makes 1 glass.

Ingredients:
- ◊ 6 ounces half-and-half
- ◊ 2 tablespoons freshly squeezed key lime juice (regular lime juice may be used instead)
- ◊ 1 tablespoon powdered gelatin (unflavored)
- ◊ 1 teaspoon lime zest
- ◊ 1 teaspoon vanilla extract
- ◊ 6 drops liquid stevia (sweetener)
- ◊ 6 ice cubes

Instructions:

Mix gelatin and half-and-half in a blender.

Add remaining ingredients except ice cubes. Blend for about a minute until well mixed.

Add ice cubes and blend until smoothie thickens.

Serve immediately.

One glass contains:

- ⊕ Calories: 280
- ⊕ Fat: 20g
- ⊕ Protein: 12g
- ⊕ Sodium: 91mg
- ⊕ Fiber: 2g
- ⊕ Carbohydrates: 17g
- ⊕ Sugar: 3g

73

Peanut Butter Cup Smoothie

This is the drinkable version of the candy treat, minus the sugar. Takes just 5 minutes to prepare, no cooking needed. Makes 1 glass.

Ingredients:
- ◊ 1/2 can coconut milk
- ◊ 1 tablespoon powdered gelatin (unflavored)
- ◊ 2 tablespoons cocoa powder
- ◊ 2 tablespoons peanut butter
- ◊ 1 teaspoon vanilla extract
- ◊ 6 drops liquid stevia
- ◊ 4 ice cubes

Instructions:

Pour gelatin and milk into a blender and pulse.

Add remaining ingredients except ice cubes; blend for another minute until well mixed.

Place ice cubes into blender and process until smoothie thickens.

Serve immediately.

A glass contains:

- ⊕ Calories: 622
- ⊕ Fat: 58g
- ⊕ Protein: 20g
- ⊕ Sodium: 189mg
- ⊕ Fiber: 6g
- ⊕ Carbohydrates: 18g
- ⊕ Sugar: 4g

74

Very Vanilla Smoothie

Not your ordinary plain vanilla milkshake. Takes 5 minutes to prepare, no cooking needed. Makes 1 glass.

Ingredients:
◊   6 ounces half-and-half
◊   1 tablespoon powdered gelatin (unflavored)
◊   1 teaspoon vanilla extract
◊   1 vanilla bean, scraped, pulp only
◊   4 drops sweetener (liquid stevia)
◊   6 ice cubes

Instructions:
Pour gelatin and half-and-half into a blender, and mix.

Add remaining ingredients except ice cubes, then blend for another minute.

Place ice cubes into blender and process until smoothie thickens.

Serve immediately.

On glass contains:
⊕   Calories: 274
⊕   Fat: 19g
⊕   Protein: 11g
⊕   Sodium: 83mg
⊕   Carbohydrates: 8g
⊕   Sugar: 1g

75

Cinnamon Roll Smoothie

Quenches your thirst and takes care of your sugar cravings. Takes 5 minutes to prepare, makes 1 glass.

Ingredients:
- ◊ 6 ounces half-and-half
- ◊ 1 tablespoon softened cream cheese
- ◊ 1 teaspoon vanilla extract
- ◊ Cinnamon: 1/2 teaspoon and 1/8 teaspoon, separately
- ◊ 6 drops liquid stevia sweetener
- ◊ 6 ice cubes

Instructions:
Blend half-and-half and cream cheese in a blender.

Put in vanilla, 1/2 teaspoon cinnamon and stevia, and blend again for another minute or so.

Add ice cubes in blender and process until smoothie thickens.

Sprinkle 1/8 teaspoon cinnamon on top and serve.

One glass contains:

- ⊕ Calories: 283
- ⊕ Fat: 24g
- ⊕ Protein: 6g
- ⊕ Sodium: 116mg
- ⊕ Fiber: 1g
- ⊕ Carbohydrates: 9g
- ⊕ Sugar: 1g

76

Creamy Mexican Hot Chocolate

This favorite Mexican drink is rich, thick and has a touch of cinnamon flavor. It has been modified to have zero sugar content. It is best enjoyed outdoors at night in front of a campfire. It takes about 3 minutes to prepare, plus 5 minutes to cook. This makes two servings.

Ingredients:
- ◊ 1 cup water
- ◊ 1 cup heavy cream
- ◊ 2 drops Stevia glycerite, or 2 teaspoons granular Swerve
- ◊ 1/3 cup cocoa powder
- ◊ 1 teaspoon cinnamon
- ◊ 1/8 teaspoon vanilla extract
- ◊ 4 tablespoons unsweetened whipped cream

Instructions:

Place a small saucepan over very low heat, and pour in all ingredients except the whipped cream.

Heat for about five minutes, or until cocoa powder is completely dissolved, with constant stirring. Ensure that the mixture does not reach boiling point. To serve, pour chocolate into two cups and top each with whipped cream.

One cup contains:

- ⊕ Calories: 538
- ⊕ Fat: 56g
- ⊕ Protein: 6g
- ⊕ Sodium: 63mg
- ⊕ Fiber: 5g
- ⊕ Carbohydrates: 17g

77

Strawberry Vanilla Smoothie

Great Keto substitute for the good ol' strawberry milkshake. Takes only 5 minutes to prepare, no cooking needed. Makes 1 glass.

Ingredients:
- ◊ 1/2 can coconut milk
- ◊ 1/4 cup chopped fresh strawberries
- ◊ 1 tablespoon powdered gelatin (unflavored)
- ◊ 1 tablespoon coconut oil, softened but not melted
- ◊ 1 teaspoon vanilla extract
- ◊ 6 drops liquid stevia
- ◊ 6 ice cubes

Instructions:
Use a blender to mix milk and gelatin.

Add remaining ingredients except ice cubes and blend for another minute until well mixed.

Add ice cubes and pulse until smoothie thickens. Serve immediately.

A glass contains:
- ⊕ Calories: 540
- ⊕ Fat: 54g
- ⊕ Protein: 10g
- ⊕ Sodium: 39mg
- ⊕ Fiber: 1g
- ⊕ Carbohydrates: 9g
- ⊕ Sugar: 2g

78

Thai Iced Coffee

This tasty drink found in every Thai restaurant and Thai home has been modified here to still be sweet and flavorful, minus the sugar and with added healthy fats It takes about 5 minutes to prepare, with no cooking time needed. This makes two servings.

Ingredients:
◊ 4 cups strong brewed coffee, cooled
◊ 3 drops stevia glycerite or 4 teaspoons erythritol or granular Swerve
◊ 2 tablespoons coconut milk
◊ 1/8 teaspoon vanilla extract
◊ 4 tablespoons heavy cream

Instructions:
Pour cooled coffee into a large bowl. Mix in the sweetener, vanilla and coconut milk. Pour the mixture in 2 tall glasses and add ice. Pour cream on top of coffee. Do not stir so that layers remain separate. Serve immediately with a tall spoon and a straw.

One glass contains:
⊕ Calories: 548
⊕ Fat: 15g
⊕ Protein: 22g
⊕ Sodium: 77mg
⊕ Carbohydrates: 80g

79

Tibetan Butter Tea (Po Cha)

Po Cha is traditionally made using yak butter and tea leaves. This is a recreation of the Tibetan staple that doesn't require you to find yak butter. It's flavorful and a great source of warmth and energy. It can be taken like coffee to start your day, or enjoyed anytime of the day, multiple times. It takes about 3 minutes to prepare and 8 minutes to cook. This recipe makes two servings.

Ingredients:
- ◊ 4 cups water
- ◊ 2 tablespoons black tea leaves
- ◊ 2 tablespoons butter
- ◊ 2 tablespoons heavy cream
- ◊ 1/8 teaspoon sea salt
- ◊ 1 drop smoke flavor

Instructions:
Bring water to boil in a small saucepan, then decrease the heat to low. Add tea leaves and simmer about three minutes. Strain. Mix the brewed tea with remaining ingredients in a blender, and mix on high for about three minutes. Serve immediately.

Each serving (cup) contains:
- ⊕ Calories: 153
- ⊕ Fat: 17g
- ⊕ Sodium: 169mg

80

Gingerbread Gem Smoothie

You don't need to wait til Christmas to enjoy this delicious gingerbread smoothie. Takes 5 minutes to prepare. Makes 1 glass.

Ingredients:
- ◊ 6 ounces almond milk (unsweetened)
- ◊ 1 tablespoon powdered gelatin (unflavored)
- ◊ 1 tablespoon almond butter
- ◊ 1/2 teaspoon ground ginger
- ◊ 1/2 teaspoon vanilla extract
- ◊ 1/2 teaspoon cinnamon
- ◊ 6 drops liquid stevia
- ◊ 6 ice cubes

Instructions:

Using a blender, mix milk and gelatin well.

Add remaining ingredients except ice cubes and blend another minute until well mixed.

Place ice cubes into blender and pulse until smoothie thickens. Serve immediately.

A glass contains:

- ⊕ Calories: 221
- ⊕ Fat: 11g
- ⊕ Protein: 16g
- ⊕ Sodium: 174mg
- ⊕ Fiber: 3g
- ⊕ Carbohydrates: 16g
- ⊕ Sugar: 9g

81

Amaretto Chilled Coffee

A refreshing cool drink that's perfect for summer nights. Takes 8 minutes to prepare. Makes 2 glasses.

Ingredients:
- ◊ 2 cups cooled brewed coffee
- ◊ Sweetener: 4 teaspoons erythritol or granular Swerve, or 3 drops stevia glycerite, divided
- ◊ 4 drops amaretto flavor, divided
- ◊ 1/2 cup heavy cream, chilled
- ◊ 1 teaspoon crumbled roasted almonds

Instructions:

Pour coffee into a medium bowl and mix with half the sweetener and half the amaretto flavor.

In a blender, add chilled heavy cream, the remaining sweetener and the remaining amaretto flavor. Blend on high until cream is whipped.

When ready to serve, pour coffee mix over ice in 2 glasses.

Spoon whipped cream on top of each coffee mix. Decorate with chopped almonds.

Serve immediately with a spoon and a straw.

One glass contains:

- ⊕ Calories: 421
- ⊕ Fat: 23g
- ⊕ Protein: 12g
- ⊕ Sodium: 55mg
- ⊕ Carbohydrates: 45g

- SECTION 10 -

DIPS AND DRESSINGS

82

Guacamole Dip

A simple Keto version of the favorite Southwestern dip. Takes 5 minutes to prepare, makes 4 servings.

Ingredients:

◊ 1 large avocado, pitted, peeled, and diced
◊ 2 large cloves garlic, minced
◊ 1 tablespoon freshly squeezed lime juice
◊ 1/2 teaspoon salt
◊ 1 small Anaheim chili pepper, diced
◊ 1/2 small yellow onion, peeled and diced
◊ 1 small vine-ripened tomato, diced
◊ 2 tablespoons freshly chopped cilantro

Instructions:

Place avocado in a small bowl together with the salt, lime juice, and garlic.

Mash avocado gently using a fork or a potato masher.

Put in chili pepper, tomato, cilantro and onion, and gently fold into mixture.

Serve immediately, or chill first in the refrigerator.

One serving contains:
- ⊕ Calories: 93
- ⊕ Fat: 7g
- ⊕ Protein: 2g
- ⊕ Sodium: 302mg
- ⊕ Fiber: 4g
- ⊕ Carbohydrates: 7g
- ⊕ Sugar: 2g

83

Bacon Olive Spread

Great on celery sticks and cucumber slices. Take 8 minutes to prepare, 10 minutes to cook. Makes 4 servings.

Ingredients:
- ◊ 4 slices bacon
- ◊ 24 Spanish olives, sliced
- ◊ 8 ounces cream cheese, softened to room temperature
- ◊ 2 tablespoons olive oil mayonnaise
- ◊ 1 tablespoon freshly squeezed lemon juice

Instructions:

Cook bacon over medium heat in a large skillet for 5 minutes on each side, or until crisp. Drain on paper towel to remove excess oil.

In a medium mixing bowl, beat softened cream cheese until smooth.

Add mayonnaise and lemon juice; mix well.

Crumble bacon into bowl, then add in the sliced olives.

Fold bacon and olives into cream cheese mixture by hand using a rubber spatula.

Serve immediately or cool first in the refrigerator.

Each serving contains:

- ⊕ Calories: 187
- ⊕ Fat: 18g
- ⊕ Protein: 3g
- ⊕ Sodium: 319mg
- ⊕ Fiber: 0g
- ⊕ Carbohydrates: 2g
- ⊕ Sugar: 1g

84

Simple Keto Mayonnaise

Takes 1 hour and 5 minutes to prepare, makes 16 servings

Ingredients:
◊ 8 ounces of any of these oils: extra-virgin olive oil, MCT, walnut oil, macadamia oil
◊ 1 large egg
◊ 2 teaspoons apple cider vinegar
◊ 1/4 teaspoon salt
◊ 1/8 teaspoon granulated garlic
◊ 1/8 teaspoon freshly ground black pepper

Instructions:
Pour oil into large-mouthed, quart-sized jar.

Add vinegar, egg and spices. Blend using an immersion blender for about 20 seconds, until mixture begins to firm up and become white.

Place lid on jar, put in refrigerator to congeal for later use as a versatile spread for wraps, a base for salad dressing, or as a binder for cheese- or nut-crusted fish.

Each serving contains:
⊕ Calories: 128
⊕ Fat: 14g
⊕ Sodium: 42mg

85

Hail Caesar Dressing

Takes 5 minutes to prepare, makes 16 servings

Ingredients:
- ◊ 1/2 medium lemon, juiced
- ◊ 1/2 tablespoon apple cider vinegar
- ◊ 1 large clove garlic, smashed
- ◊ 1 large egg, at room temperature
- ◊ 1/2 ounce anchovies
- ◊ 1/4 teaspoon salt
- ◊ 1/4 teaspoon freshly ground black pepper
- ◊ 1 cup extra-virgin olive oil

Instructions:

Put all ingredients, except oil, inside a wide-mouthed, quart-sized jar.

Mix using an immersion blender until well chopped and blended.

Add oil and blend for 20 to 30 seconds more, until the consistency of thin mayonnaise is achieved.

Chill until ready to use. Mix before use.

Each serving contains:
- ⊕ Calories: 126
- ⊕ Fat: 14g
- ⊕ Protein: 1g
- ⊕ Sodium: 74mg

86

Mojo de Ajo Aioli

A Mexican and Latin spread or dip that has been described as "the nectar of the gods." Takes 1 hour and 40 minutes to prepare, and an additional 1 hour and 10 minutes to cook. Makes 16 servings.

Ingredients:
- ◊ 1 large head garlic
- ◊ 8 ounces extra-virgin olive oil
- ◊ 1/4 teaspoon salt
- ◊ 1/4 cup lime juice
- ◊ 1 large egg
- ◊ 1/8 teaspoon cayenne pepper

Instructions:
Preheat oven to 325°F.

Separate garlic cloves and peel each one.

Fill an 8" × 8" glass casserole dish with olive oil, salt, and garlic, such that cloves are fully submerged in the olive oil.

Bake for 45 to 50 minutes until garlic is becomes light brown. Add lime juice and bake for 20 more minutes.

Remove from oven and let cool.

Once at room temperature, smash garlic with fork or potato masher. Pour oil and garlic into a large-mouthed, quart-sized Mason jar. Add egg and cayenne. Blend for about 30 seconds using an immersion blender until mixture starts to firm up and turn white.

Place cap on jar and put in refrigerator to firm up for later use as a spread on lettuce wraps or a dip for vegetables.

Each serving contains:
- ⊕ Calories: 130
- ⊕ Fat: 14g
- ⊕ Sodium: 42mg
- ⊕ Carbohydrates: 1g

- SECTION 11 -

FROZEN TREATS

87

Almond Cookie Popsicles

Sweet, creamy and 100% Keto-approved. Takes 8 to 12 hours to prepare, makes 8 servings.

Ingredients:
- ◊ 1 1/2 cups coconut cream, chilled
- ◊ 1/2 cup almond butter
- ◊ 1 teaspoon vanilla extract
- ◊ 1/4 cup erythritol or granular Swerve

Instructions:
Put all ingredients in a blender and process for about 30 seconds until completely blended.

Pour mix into 8 popsicle molds. If there are air bubbles, tap molds to remove them.

Freeze overnight or for at least 8 hours.

Remove popsicles from molds. (You may need to briefly dip the molds in hot water to loosen hard-to-remove popsicles.)

One popsicle contains:
- ⊕ Calories: 294
- ⊕ Fat: 17g
- ⊕ Protein: 5g
- ⊕ Sodium: 94mg
- ⊕ Fiber: 1g
- ⊕ Carbohydrates: 39g
- ⊕ Sugar: 30g

88

Frozen Maca-Nutty Bits

A guilt-free snack for nutty chocolate lovers. Takes 3 hours to prepare, and 5 minutes to cook. Makes 12 servings.

Ingredients:
- ◊ 12 whole macadamia nuts
- ◊ 1/4 cup almond butter
- ◊ 1/4 cup coconut oil
- ◊ 2 tablespoons cocoa powder
- ◊ 1 teaspoon vanilla extract
- ◊ 12 drops liquid stevia

Instructions:

Combine coconut oil, almond butter, stevia and vanilla in a small saucepan, and cook over medium heat. Stir often until all ingredients melt, then turn off heat.

Add cocoa powder, and stir in well.

Pour mixture into 12 molds of an ice cube tray or candy mold tray, until about 2/3 full. (For best results, use molds with a silicon bottom.)

Place 1 macadamia nut into each filled mold.

Freeze until set. Serve frozen.

Once serving contains:

- ⊕ Calories: 93
- ⊕ Fat: 9g
- ⊕ Protein: 2g
- ⊕ Sodium: 25mg
- ⊕ Fiber: 1g
- ⊕ Carbohydrates: 2g
- ⊕ Sugar: 1g

89

Hazelnut Cappuccino Popsicles

The frozen version of the coffee favorite. Takes 8 to 12 hours to prepare, and 1 minute to cook. Makes 8 servings.

Ingredients:
- ◊ 1 cup brewed strong coffee or espresso
- ◊ 1 cup heavy whipping cream
- ◊ 1/2 cup crumbled hazelnuts
- ◊ 1/8 teaspoon hazelnut flavor
- ◊ 1/4 cup erythritol or granular Swerve

Instructions:

Place all ingredients except the hazelnuts in a blender. Process for about 30 seconds until completely mixed.

Pour mix into 8 popsicle molds; if there are air bubbles, tap molds to remove them.

Freeze overnight or for at least 8 hours.

In a small nonstick pan, toast crumbled hazelnuts over medium heat for about 1 minute, stirring frequently.

Remove popsicles from molds.

Before serving, press popsicles into hazelnut crumbles so they coat the outside.

One popsicle contains:

- ⊕ Calories: 148
- ⊕ Fat: 15g
- ⊕ Protein: 2g
- ⊕ Sodium: 11mg
- ⊕ Fiber: 1g
- ⊕ Carbohydrates: 8g

90

Frozen Orange Creamsicle

The Keto version of the old fashioned frozen favorite. Takes 3 hours to prepare, no cooking needed. Makes 12 servings.

Ingredients:
- ◊ 1/4 cup heavy whipping cream
- ◊ 1/4 cup coconut oil
- ◊ 2 ounces cream cheese, softened
- ◊ 2 tablespoons freshly squeezed orange juice
- ◊ 1 tablespoon orange zest
- ◊ 12 drops liquid stevia

Instructions:

Combine all ingredients in a small bowl or wide-mouthed jar. Blend for about 30 seconds with an immersion blender.

Place mixture in 12 molds of a candy mold tray (preferably a silicone tray).

Freeze until set.

One serving contains:
- ⊕ Calories: 75
- ⊕ Fat: 8g
- ⊕ Sodium: 17mg
- ⊕ Carbohydrates: 1g

91

Frozen Butter Rum Chocolate

Keto-compliant, dairy-free and almost alcohol-free. Takes 3 hours to prepare, and 5 minutes to cook. Makes 12 servings.

Ingredients:
- ◊ 1/4 cup almond butter
- ◊ 1/4 cup coconut oil
- ◊ 2 tablespoons cocoa powder
- ◊ 2 teaspoons rum extract
- ◊ 12 drops liquid stevia

Instructions:

In a small saucepan and over medium heat, combine all ingredients except cocoa powder. Stirring frequently until ingredients have melted. Turn off heat.

Stir in cocoa powder and mix well.

Pour mixture into 12 molds of an ice cube tray or candy mold tray (silicon-bottomed if possible) until about 3/4 full.

Place in freezer.

One serving contains:

- ⊕ Calories: 75
- ⊕ Fat: 7g
- ⊕ Protein: 2g
- ⊕ Sodium: 25mg
- ⊕ Fiber: 1g
- ⊕ Carbohydrates: 2g
- ⊕ Sugar: 1g

92

Frozen Coconut White Chocolate

Another tasty frozen treat that takes 3 hours to prepare and 5 minutes to cook. Makes 12 servings.

Ingredients:
- ◊ 1/4 cup cocoa butter
- ◊ 1/4 cup coconut oil
- ◊ 1 teaspoon vanilla extract
- ◊ 12 drops liquid stevia
- ◊ 1 tablespoon unsweetened coconut, shredded

Instructions:

Combine cocoa butter, coconut oil, vanilla, and stevia in a small saucepan. Cook over medium heat, stirring often until ingredients have melted. Turn off heat.

Add coconut in and mix well.

Pour mixture into 12 molds of an ice cube tray or candy mold tray until about 3/4 full.

Freeze and serve.

One serving contains:
- ⊕ Calories: 82
- ⊕ Fat: 9g

- SECTION 12 -

MISCELLANEOUS

93

Ham and Cheese Roll

(Makes 8 servings)

Ingredients:
- ◊ 2 1/4 oz deviled ham
- ◊ 2 cups Cheddar cheese, shredded
- ◊ 8 oz cream cheese, softened
- ◊ 1 tablespoon parsley flakes
- ◊ 1 teaspoon grated onions
- ◊ 1 teaspoon dry mustard
- ◊ 1/2 teaspoon paprika
- ◊ 1/2 cup pecans
- ◊ Chopped parsley sprigs to garnish

Instructions:

Set aside the parsley and pecans, and combine all the other ingredients.

Mix them well and chill in the fridge for at least an hour.

Shape mixture into rolls, approximately 8-inch long, and then coat with pecans.

Garnish with parsley.

May be served with diet or low-carb crackers.

One serving contains:
- ⊕ Total Net carbs: 2 grams

94

Fake Macaroni and Cheese

Pasta and macaroni aren't Keto-compliant, but you can fake the taste of mac-and-cheese with this delicious substitute. This makes 4 servings.

Ingredients:
- ◊ 1 lb. tofu (should be firm, such as "cotton" tofu)
- ◊ 2 medium eggs
- ◊ 2 cups Cheddar cheese
- ◊ 1/4 cup heavy cream
- ◊ Spices to add taste: salt, pepper, onion powder, garlic powder, nutmeg, dry mustard, cayenne

Instructions:

Drain tofu very well, squeezing out all moisture. Slice into small pieces, all of the same size as much as possible.

In another bowl, mix together eggs, cheese and cream.

Stir tofu pieces into mixture and add the spices and seasonings. Add generous amounts of these to liven up the tofu which is usually bland.

Transfer mixture to a casserole dish or a lightly greased baking plate, and bake for 30 to 45 minutes at 375 degrees, or until the mixture turns into a golden brown color.

Each serving contains:
- ⊕ Net carbs: 2.6 grams

95

Spaghetti Squash Lasagna

(Makes 4 servings)

Ingredients:

- ◊ 1 ½ cups spaghetti squash
- ◊ 1 lb ground beef
- ◊ 1 cup Parmesan cheese, grated
- ◊ 2 cups mozzarella cheese, shredded
- ◊ 1 teaspoon chili powder
- ◊ ¾ jar (regular size) pasta sauce
- ◊ 1 egg
- ◊ ½ teaspoon basil
- ◊ ½ teaspoon oregano
- ◊ 1 teaspoon red pepper flakes
- ◊ 2 cloves of garlic, minced
- ◊ Sea salt to taste

Instructions:

Microwave spaghetti squash for about 20 minutes. Then allow to sit for 5 minutes.

Place red pepper flakes and sauce in a saucepan, mix, and let this simmer on the stove, with lid on.

Combine meatball ingredients in a medium bowl, then roll into small meatballs.

Melt butter or ghee on a large frying pan on medium heat. Cook meatballs here and cover. When one side is browned, flip and cook the other side. Each side should cook for 3-5 minutes.

Add cooked meatballs, after removing any adhering oil or grease, to the sauce.

Halve the squash, remove seeds and guts, and scrape out 2 ½ cups of spaghetti squash. Set aside.

In a deep and narrow rectangular baking pan, layer sauce, squash spaghetti, meatballs, sauce and mozzarella.

Bake at 350F for about 30 minutes.

Each serving contains:
   ⊕ Net carbs: 9

96

Ham-Asparagus Brunch Cake

(Makes 10 servings)

Ingredients:

- ◊ 1 1/2 cups fresh asparagus, cut
- ◊ 2 cups cooked ham, chopped
- ◊ 3 tablespoons green onion, sliced
- ◊ 2 tablespoons butter
- ◊ 6 eggs
- ◊ 1/3 cup heavy cream
- ◊ 1 teaspoon dried mustard
- ◊ 1/4 teaspoon salt
- ◊ 1/4 teaspoon pepper
- ◊ 6 ounces Cheddar cheese, shredded

Instructions:

Preheat oven to 350.

In a large skillet, melt butter over medium heat, and cook asparagus and onions for about 3 minutes.

In a large mixing bowl, stir together cream, eggs and seasonings.

Place cooked onions, asparagus and ham into a baking dish and pour egg mixture on top.

Bake for 10 to 15 minutes. When done, sprinkle cheese on top to taste.

Each serving contains:

- ⊕ Total Net carbs: 2 grams

97

Mexican Veal Sausages

(Makes 4 servings)

Ingredients:
- ◊ 1 1/2 pounds ground veal
- ◊ 2 tablespoons green or red salsa
- ◊ 2 green onions, finely chopped (should make about 1/3 cup)
- ◊ 2 tablespoons fresh cilantro, chopped
- ◊ 2 tablespoons olive oil
- ◊ 1/2 teaspoon ground cumin
- ◊ 1/2 teaspoon salt
- ◊ 1/4 teaspoon freshly ground black pepper

For the garnishing:
- ◊ 1/4 cup green or red salsa
- ◊ 1/4 cup sour cream
- ◊ 1 lime, cut into wedges or slices

Instructions:

Combine veal, onion and all spices in a mixing bowl. Blend together, preferably by mashing together using the bare hands.

Shape mixture into 4 sausage links.

Pour oil in a nonstick skillet, put on high heat and cook sausages for 8-10 minutes, turning frequently, until they brown.

One serving contains:
- ⊕ Total Net carbs: 0.5 gram

98

Stir-Fried Chicken and Bacon Sausage

(Makes 3 servings)

Ingredients:
- ◊ 4 chicken sausages (or bacon-and-cheese chicken sausages)
- ◊ 3 cups broccoli florets
- ◊ 3 cups spinach
- ◊ 1/2 cup Parmesan cheese
- ◊ 1/2 cup tomato sauce
- ◊ 1/4 cup red wine
- ◊ 2 tablespoon salted butter
- ◊ 2 teaspoon garlic, minced
- ◊ ½ teaspoon red pepper flakes

Instructions:

Slice the chicken sausages.

Place water in a medium pot, put on stove over high heat. While waiting for it to boil, place sausage slices on a pan on high heat. Stir sausages until they brown on both sides.

Add broccoli to the boiling water and cook for 3-5 minutes or until desired doneness is achieved. Remove water and set broccoli aside.

Move browned sausages to one side of the pan, then add in the butter, and then the garlic. Saute for 1 minute. Mix together with the sausage slices, and then add the broccoli.

Pour in the red wine and tomato sauce, and then the red pepper flakes.

Mix together, add spinach, salt and pepper.

Simmer this for 5-10 minutes, and allow to cool.

Just before serving, add fresh parmesan cheese over the top and allow it to melt.

Each serving contains:
- ⊕ 450 Calories
- ⊕ Fats: 28g
- ⊕ Net carbs: 7g
- ⊕ Protein: 36g

99

Country Herbed Meatloaf

(Makes 9 servings)

Ingredients:

For the herb sauce:
- ◊ 8 ounces fresh mushrooms, chopped
- ◊ 1 (28 oz) can crushed tomatoes
- ◊ 1 (6 oz) can tomato paste
- ◊ 1/4 cup olive oil
- ◊ 1 large onion, finely chopped
- ◊ 1 garlic clove, minced
- ◊ 1 teaspoon salt
- ◊ 1/8 teaspoon pepper
- ◊ 1 cup water
- ◊ 1 bay leaf
- ◊ 2 tablespoons fresh basil (or 2 teaspoons if dried, chopped)
- ◊ 2 Splenda packets

For the meatloaf:
- ◊ 2 lb ground beef (Another option is to use any combination of ground beef, veal and pork)
- ◊ 1 cup pork rinds, crushed
- ◊ 2 eggs, beaten

Instructions:

Sauté mushrooms, onions and garlic in an oiled skillet over high heat.

Add tomatoes, tomato paste, salt, pepper and Splenda. Stir together.

Remove from heat and set aside 1-1/2 cups of sauce mixture.

Add in water, basil and bay leaf.

Bring to a boil, lower heat, cover and simmer for 45 minutes.

Combine eggs, meat and pork rinds with the herb sauce that was set aside earlier.

Press into roasting or loaf pan, and bake for 45 minutes at 350 degrees.

Take out loaf from oven, drain, and spread the simmered herb sauce over loaf.

Put back into the oven for an additional 15 minutes.

Remove bay leaf.

Pour left-over sauce on top, and serve.

Each serving contains:
  ⊕ Total Net carbs: 4 grams

100

Simple Turkey Broccoli Casserole

(Makes 8 servings)

Ingredients:
- ◊ 2 packages frozen broccoli (10 oz each)
- ◊ 2 cups cooked turkey, diced
- ◊ 1 (10 oz) can cream of mushroom soup
- ◊ 1/2 cup Cheddar cheese, grated
- ◊ 1/2 cup heavy cream

Instructions:

Preheat oven to 375F.

Cook broccoli according to package instructions.

Layer broccoli in a baking dish and spread turkey on top.

Mix soup with cream and pour on top of turkey. Sprinkle grated cheese on top.

Place in oven and bake for about 30 minutes.

Serve hot.

Each serving contains:
- ⊕ Total Net carbs: 7 grams

Conclusion

In Conclusion, I would like to thank you once again for taking action by purchasing this book. I hope this book shall help you achieve your wellbeing objectives. Wishing you all the best and good luck!

Printed in Poland
by Amazon Fulfillment
Poland Sp. z o.o., Wrocław